First **BBC**

Top of the

compiled by Boswell Taylor

This is the book of the television programme that now spans the globe – a book that will give the reader hours of entertainment, while he teaches himself about the world around us, and tests his wits.

Also available in Knight Books
Second BBC tv Top of the Form quiz book
Third BBC tv Top of the Form quiz book
Fourth BBC tv Top of the Form quiz book

#/

First BBC tv
Top of the Form
Quiz Book

compiled by Boswell Taylor

 Knight Books

the paperback division of Brockhampton Press

by arrangement with the British Broadcasting Corporation

The publishers would like to express their
gratitude for all the help in the making
of this book received from the BBC
Outside Broadcasts Department, and in
particular from Peter Dimmock,
Bill Wright and Mary Evans.

ISBN 0 340 04140 4

First published April 1968 by Knight Books,
the paperback division of Brockhampton Press Ltd, Leicester
under the title *BBC tv Top of the Form Quiz Book*
Tenth impression 1973

Printed and bound in Great Britain by
Cox & Wyman Ltd, London, Reading and Fakenham

Text copyright © 1968 Boswell Taylor
Drawings by Leslie Marshall © 1968 by Brockhampton Press Ltd

Photographs and cartoon drawings © 1968
British Broadcasting Corporation

Contents

Introduction by Peter Dimmock

*General Manager,
BBC tv Outside
Broadcasts Group*

At a touch of the magic switch in BBC Television Centre the signature tune of *Top of the Form* can be heard in more than eight million homes throughout the length and breadth of the land. One more edition of this ever popular programme is on the screen. What is the appeal of this quiz programme that began in radio in 1948, and has gathered momentum and popularity through six years of television, where it has been so ably and successfully fostered by executive producer Bill Wright and producer Mary Evans?

Mainly it is the participants, their freshness, their good-humour, their spontaneity and their scholarship. It is invidious to select examples, perhaps, but who could forget Graham Williamson's remarkably complete and yet succinct definition of the Menshevik-Bolshevik crisis in the Russian Revolution, or Gregory Willis's description of the geologist's 'iron hat' or Peter Gough's explanation of a 'fair catch' in rugby football?

Behind this spontaneity is a tremendous amount of engineering. The co-operation of the G.P.O. is required for 'lines' from London to the central studio and to the mobile studios at the schools. In the central studio alone there can be as many as thirty engineers and other workers; while altogether, to ensure the smooth production of this technically-complicated programme, there may be a hundred people involved.

The programme has to be carefully planned, and the initial stages are taken months ahead, with the selection of the teams. Dossiers are compiled about each competitor giving details of syllabuses, hobbies, reading, religion and so on. This material goes to the Question Setter, Boswell Taylor, who also interviews the teams. From these combined efforts a balanced script is produced and thoroughly researched to ensure accuracy.

Before each programme takes place a full briefing is held when the script is discussed in detail, with the Question Masters anxious that the schools they represent have an absolutely fair deal. The Question Masters become identified with their teams, so much so that on one occasion after Geoffrey Wheeler had had a run of several defeats the milkman said to Mrs Wheeler, 'I see we lost again last night.'

Despite planning, we can never be sure of the response to a question. There is the Australian boy who described the English Channel as '100 miles wide and the English often swim it'; the girl who suggested that a Scotch egg was 'an egg fried in batter and Scotch whisky'; the boy who said that a 'hack writer was a writer who wrote about horses'.

And last year the programme joined the Space Age.

The two schools taking part were 12,000 miles apart plus a time differential of nine hours. It was morning in the United Kingdom and 7 o'clock in the evening in Australia. Spring in the United Kingdom and autumn in Australia. And yet the production facilities of the BBC met this technical challenge with supreme success.

Following the first successful Transworld *Top of the Form* series, a United Kingdom team visited Expo '67 in Montreal to compete against the Canadian National Champions of their quiz programme *Reach for the Top*.

Future transworld series are planned so that, linked by Space Age communications, the youth of the nations can talk to each other – and to us – across the continents and oceans of the world.

How to use this book

Top of the Form aims at entertainment first and erudition second. The two have a way of merging.

It is fun to match your wits against another's. To learn interesting items of information is fun too. (Did you know before that the snake's organ of smell is that terrifying forked tongue?)

To find oneself scampering to the encyclopaedia and tracking down a fact that you feel sure can't be right – that's fun! And to lose oneself in a wonderful 'browsing' session, going from peregrines to porcupines, or from snakes to sundials (now I know why our sundial doesn't register the correct time!), from Alfred the Great to astronaut – that's fun, too!

This book has been devised to contain the elements that have made *Top of the Form* such a popular programme. Here are the graded questions to give everyone – even the youngest member of the family – a chance. The quickies have become 'Speed quizzes'. And while there are some classified sets of questions, there are also plenty of general knowledge sets, because part of the fun of a quiz is not knowing what topic will be the next to emerge.

To provide team competition you will find double pages of balanced questions, usually graded in difficulty, too. A reviewer once suggested of a BBC Television *Top of the Form* programme that the questions must have been put through a computer, they were so accurately balanced. They have certainly not been computerized, but it is hoped that the balance is sufficiently true to give fair and enjoyable team contests.

The questions, you will notice, are grouped in sets. The answers however have been numbered in sequence for ease of reference. Many of you may feel that the full information given in the answers has its own value quite apart from verifying – or otherwise – your answers.

You may accept the individual challenge of the questions. You may play against the clock. You may compete as a family or as members of a Youth Club or Scouts or Guides. You may use the book as a brain-teaser at school. You may find the questions useful in party games. But in whatever way you use the book – have fun! And in having fun let's hope you will find the questions stimulating, too.

On your own

There are plenty of opportunities for variety for the player who wishes to meet the challenge of the questions by himself. He can use the questions to test his knowledge of the subjects that interest him. He may wish to test his vocabulary power, and discover whether, besides knowing the general meaning of the words, he knows their precise definition.

He can make a team game of it and, at the same time, test our claim for balanced questions. He will have to be Team A and Team B in turn and forget bonuses.

I suggest you have dictionary and encyclopaedia close at hand, but only score a single point if you have to refer to either of them. All said and done, if you don't know the answer to a question the next best thing is to find it out.

Team quizzes

The book lends itself admirably to team contests, and the grading is sufficiently wide for everyone to have a chance.

As all the contestants will probably be in one room, only one

Question Master will be needed, and he can act as judge and scorer as well.

We never have an exact time limit for an answer, and the Question Master at home will probably find it simpler to use his own judgement than to work to the clock. Remember that half the fun is in the slickness of the reply, and the game might flag if the contestants are allowed too long to answer. In any case, do not allow extra time when the question is put across for a bonus; the contestant has had the time given to his opponent already to formulate a reply.

In order to maintain the party spirit you may like to award a point to those contestants who provide a witty answer instead of the correct one. The wittier and funnier the better. But the game defeats one of its purposes if you do not read out the correct answer afterwards.

It is not a bad plan to make a point of always reading out the answer in the book so that precise definitions are supplied.

The format of the book is especially kind to teams of varied ability. Particularly in the team quizzes the questions are so arranged that the simplest questions come first with progressively more difficult questions to follow.

Pen and paper games

A written quiz can make a restful break in a noisy party. Make sure that the contestants know exactly how many questions they will be tackling. A time limit spices the contest, but time yourself tackling the same quiz first to make sure that your assessment of the time required is fairly accurate.

A quiz makes a good party starter. The questions are typed or written out or cut out from the book and attached to cards which are numbered consecutively.

As the guests arrive they walk round the room writing out the answers they know on paper slips that have been given to them. When all the guests have arrived close the game and award the prize to the guest with the highest score of correct answers. If guests are unknown to each other you might quicken friendly relationships by making partnerships and letting them cover the course as a team.

On occasions you may have two or more guests with the exact number of correct answers. Give them a single question from the book to answer, and the winner is the first with the correct answer.

How to find out

It is sometimes said that facts themselves are not important; it is knowing where to go to find them, and the use that is made of them that is important.

While as an educationist I might support that argument, it seems to me that it is not much use knowing where to find the facts if the student is too self-satisfied with his ignorance ever to want to find out.

The competitive spice of the quiz programme, the challenge that it offers, is an incentive to finding out. A continuing interest, with the natural recourse to reference material, should sharpen the ability of the student to know where to go to get the facts he wants.

How many viewers, hearing a question that interests them, would like to know more about the subject, and haven't the slightest idea how to track the information down?

Some basic reference books are essential. The most important of all are dictionary, encyclopaedia and atlas.

A good encyclopaedia contains a compendium of information organized for ready reference. Some guidance in the use of the encyclopaedia is essential, including an alphabetic sense.

The student must know exactly what he wants to find out. The question may ease this problem by stating baldly what is required. For example, what is a 'cul-de-sac'? Obviously the clue here is 'cul-de-sac'. And now the student must make the decision whether to find out the information from the encyclopaedia or the dictionary. And if in the encyclopaedia, in which section to look. Only practice will prompt him to make the right decision. In another question the key word is not so apparent. For example, 'Who became king twice, first as the sixth and then as the first?' What is the clue here? Do we try 'king' or study the royal line of succession, and if so which royal line of succession, and where will we find it? Or do we try a hit or miss method, looking under the kings' names known to us: Edward, Charles, John, etc.?

The second necessary book of reference is the dictionary, and much that has been said about the encyclopaedia applies equally to the dictionary.

As soon as possible a dictionary that gives root meanings should be used. Once you know that the prefix 'hydro-' suggests a connection with water, you are half-way to an understanding of any word with this prefix. Many a competitor in *Top of the Form* has arrived at a correct answer by this means aided by a little common-sense.

The specialist dictionaries should not be overlooked. A paperback series that covers 'Science', 'Music', 'Art', 'Psychology', 'Building' etc. is adequate for our purpose.

Other specialist reference book series are available. For example, the pocket-sized *Observer* series (Frederick Warne) with the classification of specialized facts about nature in particular.

The Guinness Book of Records and *The Dunlop Book of Facts* are mines of information. For current affairs *Whitaker's Almanack*, *Pears* (both adult and junior editions), and *The Daily Mail Year Book* all have value. Be careful that you have the latest editions or use earlier editions with caution. Out-of-date information is inaccurate information.

This is a fair basic library but the list of source material of a specialized nature is so vast that it would be impossible to record them here. And it is not the possession of books of reference that will provide the answers; a knowledge of where to look is vital.

However, once more it should be stressed that the popular BBC Television *Top of the Form* programmes are intended to be entertainment, but if they provide the kind of entertainment that makes the increasing of personal knowledge fun – then I suggest that it is one of the best forms of fun you can have.

General knowledge 1

1 A loom is a machine used for weaving, but what is an *heirloom*?

2 A *spinet* has nothing to do with spinning. What is it?

3 What is a *microbe*?

4 What are these instruments called?

a   b   c

5 What is a *first degree burn*?

6 What is a *green-stick fracture*?

7 How was the Norman Invasion recorded for the Bishop of Bayeux?

8 How did William the Conqueror find out how much his new territories were worth?

9 What is a *jaywalker*?

10 What is a *road hog*?

11 What subject on a school timetable was named after the Latin word meaning *to know*?

12 What does the *geo* in geography and geology stand for?

13 What is the name given to the cold northerly wind that blows down the Adriatic Sea in winter?

14 What is the hot southerly wind that blows from the Sahara across southern Italy?

15 What is the common name for nitrous oxide?

16 What is solidified carbon dioxide usually known as?

17 What does an ecologist study?

18 What does a palaeontologist study?

Authors and their works

19   Who wrote *Uncle Tom's Cabin*?

20   Who wrote *Tom Brown's Schooldays*?

21   In the novel by Richard Armstrong, what was the *Lame Duck*?

22   In the novel by Henry Williamson, what was *Tarka*?

23   Who wrote a satire called *Animal Farm*?

24   Who wrote the *Just So* stories about jungle animals?

25   If you read a book by Arthur Ransome, what would you expect it to be about?

26   If you read a story by Captain W. E. Johns, what would you expect it to be about?

27   What was Patrick Reid's 'Colditz'?

28   What was Mrs Gaskell's 'Cranford'?

29   Who wrote the play called *A Man for All Seasons* and who was the 'man for all seasons'?

30   In the book *Cry, the Beloved Country*, what is the 'beloved country'?

31   Who was the blind British poet who told of the Fall of Satan?

32   Who was the blind Greek poet who told of the Siege of Troy?

33   Who wrote a novel about *White Fang* and what was it?

34   Who wrote a novel about *The Midwich Cuckoos* and what were they?

35   Who was the Scandinavian dramatist who wrote a play called *A Doll's House*?

36   Who was the Irishman who wrote the comedy called *The School for Scandal*?

37   The author of *The New Men*, a prize-winning novel, became a Parliamentary Secretary while in the House of Lords. What is his name?

38   Who was the American-born British poet who won the Nobel prize for literature in 1948? His works include *Murder in the Cathedral* and *The Cocktail Party*.

Speed quiz 1

How many can you get right in TWO minutes?

---

39 Who usually live in barracks?

40 Who usually live in a priory?

41 What country's flag   **42**   What country's flag
is this?   is this?

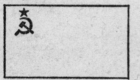 

43 Is Portugal a kingdom or a republic?

44 Is Denmark a kingdom or a republic?

45 Who, in the Bible, wore a coat of many colours?

46 Who, in the Bible, was cast into a den of lions?

47 Who live in a kraal?

48 Who lived in tepees?

49 Is the name of Brindley associated with railways or
canals?

50 Is the name of Brunel associated with railways or roads?

51 Is Pb the symbol for lead or for silver?

52 Is Au the symbol for platinum or gold?

53 What kind of fruit is a prune?

54 What kind of fruit is a sultana?

55 Was Richard I a Plantagenet or a Tudor?

56 Was Richard III of York or of Lancaster?

57 Was Leofric the husband of Guinevere or Godiva?

58 Was Desdemona the wife of Othello or the daughter of
King Lear?

Team quiz 1

59a According to the old rhyme, what is Wednesday's child?

60a Why are tent ropes slackened at night?

61a How does a hovercraft work?

62a If you apply for a job asking for a s.a.e., what must you do?

63a Where were the 'hanging gardens' which were supposed to be one of the seven wonders of the world, and what was wonderful about them?

64a What food is Caerphilly noted for?

65a We call the highest point of tide the 'spring tide'. What do we call the lowest?

66a How would you address a bench of magistrates?

67a What is the commonest source of ivory?

68a What does a botanist study?

69a Why is the keystone important in the construction of an arch?

70a What was an Elizabethan masque?

71a What is oxy-acetylene welding?

72a In which county is 'Widdicombe Fair', and what happened to 'the old grey mare' in the song?

73a How does a sailor get a ship model into a bottle?

74a What animal's skin gives us Morocco leather?

59b Solomon Grundy,
Born on a Monday
Christened on a Tuesday . . .
What happened to him on Wednesday?

60b Why are grease bands fixed round the trunks of trees in early autumn?

61b What is a bathyscaphe used for?

62b In a sales advertisement, a bicycle is offered at £10 o.n.o. What does o.n.o. stand for?

63b What is the Zuider Zee, and what is happening to it?

64b Where does Canterbury lamb come from?

65b The northern boundary of the tropics is known as the Tropic of Cancer. What is the southern boundary called?

66b How would you address an ambassador in speech?

67b What is ebony?

68b What does an ornithologist study?

69b Why is pectin important in the making of jam?

70b Who were the 'barnstormers'?

71b What is a basting stitch?

72b In which county is 'Ilkley Moor,' and what might happen to you according to the song if you do not take the singer's advice?

73b How does the pearl get in the oyster?

74b What animal's fur is made into a musquash coat?

Music and song

75 This is the first line of a well-known Christmas carol, give the second line: 'Good Christian men, rejoice . . .'

76 What follows: 'It came upon the midnight clear . . .'?

77 What kind of song is 'Blow the man down', and what kind of person would have been most likely to sing it?

78 What kind of song is 'Swing Low Sweet Chariot', and what kind of person would have been most likely to sing it?

79 Who wrote the music and lyrics for *The Sound of Music*?

80 Who wrote the music and lyrics for the hit musical *My Fair Lady*?

81 Who composed an opera about bullfighters, and what is the title of the opera?

82 Who composed an opera about an old man who sells his soul to the devil in return for youth and love, and what is the title of the opera?

83 What is *pizzicato* in violin playing?

84 If you saw the direction *legato* on a piece of music, how would you play it?

85 What is the name of the only opera composed by Beethoven?

86 Name three of the operas in Wagner's *Ring* cycle.

87 Name the composer of the music of 'Nutcracker Suite'.

88 Name the composer of the music of 'Tsar Saltan Suite'.

89 Who composed the overture 'Semiramide', and what is its connection with Babylon?

90 Who composed the music of the opera *Lohengrin*, and what is its connection with the Holy Grail?

91 Who composed the six symphonic poems entitled *My Country*, and what was the name of the country?

92 The composer of the opera *Prince Igor* fussed over it for

18 years, and at his death it was still incomplete. What is the name of the composer, and the nationality of Prince Igor?

93 'Episodes in the Life of an Artist' is the sub-title of a well-known piece of music. What is the title and who was the composer?

94 What are these musical instruments?

General knowledge 2

95 If you went to the 'Tate' in London, what would you go to see?

96 What can be seen in a *planetarium*?

97 In aviation, what is a MiG?

98 In cookery, what is an apple Charlotte?

99 What is a wind rose, and what can you find out from it?

100 What is an anemometer, and what can you find out from it?

101 How does the Youth Hostels Association help the hiker?

102 Why should a hiker be grateful to the National Trust?

103 William Penn, the Quaker, lived most of his life in England, and was buried in Buckinghamshire in 1718. Why might he be better remembered in the United States of America?

104 In mythology, Theseus killed the Minotaur, a monster with the head of a bull and body of a man. How did he escape from the Labyrinth, from which no one was supposed to be able to escape?

105 For whom was the British Legion formed?

106 By what name are the members of the Society of Friends better known?

107 What is *Afrikaans*?

108 What is *Esperanto*?

109 What is the Outward Bound Trust?

110 What is the British Volunteer Service?

111 By what name was the Women's Social and Political Union, formed by Mrs Emmeline Pankhurst in 1903, better known, and what did its members agitate to get?

112 Who was the architect responsible for the rebuilding of many of London's churches after the Great Fire?

Speed quiz 2

How many can you get right in TWO minutes?

---

113 Who, in the nursery rhyme, 'stole a pig and away he run'?

114 Who, in the nursery rhyme, had so many children she didn't know what to do?

115 What do the letters A.A. stand for?

116 What is a G.P.?

117 What does C.O.D. stand for?

118 What do the letters R.A.C. stand for?

119 Finish this phrase: 'The Great Wall of . . .'

120 Finish this phrase: 'The White Cliffs of . . .'

121 Does a snake poison its victim with its tongue or through its fangs?

122 Does a butterfly collect nectar from a flower with its legs or through its tongue?

123 What would you probably be if you were a member of the N.U.T.?

124 What would you probably be if you were a member of the B.M.A.?

125 If you saw F.R.I.B.A. on a nameplate, whose house would you be passing?

126 If you saw F.R.C.V.S. on a nameplate, whose house would you be passing?

127 What does a micrometer measure?

128 What does a galvanometer measure?

129 What animal, creature or insect do we associate with Robert the Bruce of Scotland?

130 What animal do we associate with Hannibal?

131 What drug is obtained from the poppy?

132 What drug is obtained from the cinchona tree?

Team quiz 2 – words and sayings

Words

133a What is the difference between a *colander* and a *calendar*.

134a Why should a *panacea* be just the treatment for a bad attack of housemaid's knee?

135a Is a *drugget* (i) an unqualified chemist (ii) a coarse floor covering or (iii) a deep-sea fish?

136a Why might a farmer grumble when he pays his *tithes*?

Sayings

137a Finish this saying: 'Birds of a feather . . .'

138a What is a 'bird in the hand' worth?

139a What should you do to sleeping dogs?

140a Complete this saying: 'You'll never make a silk purse . . .'

Definitions

Choose the correct definition from three choices for the words given below:

141a A *piebald* is (i) a pie without a filling, (ii) two colours irregularly arranged, or (iii) a cross between a horse and a mule.

142a *Indigo* is (i) a native of an African tribe that originally came from India, (ii) a deep blue dye, or (iii) a river in South America.

143a A *stevedore* is (i) a man employed in loading ships, (ii) a bullfighter who puts darts in the bull's back, or (iii) a wide-brimmed hat worn by Brazilians.

144a A *somnambulist* is (i) a member of the Noise Abatement Society, (ii) a medical auxiliary, or (iii) a sleep-walker.

Words

133b What is the difference between a *gorilla* and a *guerilla*?

134b Why might a choir boy be glad of a *misericord*?

135b Is a *ptarmigan* (i) a type of road surface, (ii) a bird of the grouse family or (iii) a kind of jersey?

136b Why might a person be happy to pay a *peppercorn* rent?

Sayings

137b According to the saying, what does the early bird do?

138b Finish this saying: 'Don't count your chickens ...'

139b What happens when the cat's away?

140b What do 'fine feathers' make?

Definitions

Choose the correct definition from the three choices for the words given below:

141b A *purser* is (i) an officer aboard ship who keeps the accounts, (ii) a university scholarship, or (iii) a cautious housewife.

142b An *almanac* is (i) a gift for the poor, (ii) a type of waterproof garment, or (iii) an annual calendar of months and days.

143b A *paragon* is (i) a sacred building with pyramidal towers, (ii) a four-sided figure with parallel sides, or (iii) a model of excellence.

144b A *pluviometer* is (i) a kind of computer, (ii) a rain gauge, or (iii) a measure for testing the specific gravity of wines.

145 What kind of stories did Aesop tell?
146 What kind of stories are the Brothers Grimm famous for?
147 What is *a gate-leg table*?
148 What is a *stable*, or *Dutch*, *door*?
149 What is market gardening?
150 What is a stock market?
151 What would you be unable to do if you were *illiterate*?
152 What would you be able to do if you were *bilingual*?
153 What would you deduce from the phrase: 'Joan Smith, née Brown'?
154 What would you deduce from the phrase: 'John Smith, alias Brown'?
155 In the Middle Ages what was the *elixir of life* that the alchemists sought?
156 What was the El Dorado that explorers sought?
157 What was the original purpose of the *signet ring*?
158 What was the original purpose of the *penknife*?
159 Where is this landmark and what does it do?

160 What is the difference between a *hitch* and a *splice*?
161 Where do we find a *lintel*?
162 Where do we find a *newel post*?
163 Where can you see the *aurora borealis*, and what is it?
164 Where could you see the Great Geyser, and what is it?

Sports and games 1

165 What is a 'love game' in tennis?

166 What is a 'let' in tennis?

167 What is a 'night-watchman' in cricket?

168 What is a 'scissors movement' in rugby football?

169 In what game is a shuttlecock used, and what is it?

170 In soccer, what does the '4–2–4' formation mean?

171 In what athletics event does the winning team move backwards?

172 In what event sometimes held in school sports does the winning competitor come in last?

173 What is a *bully-off*?

174 What is a *scrum*?

175 What game is played on a green?

176 What game is played on links?

177 What is a *telescopic fork*, and how does it help the motor-cyclist?

178 In which sport is a *spinnaker* used, and what is it?

179 In a boat race, what is the term for the oarsman who sets the pace?

180 What is another name for the triple jump in athletics?

181 In ski-ing, how do you do a *kick-turn*?

182 In rugby football, how do you do a *drop-kick*?

183 In what game would these be required?

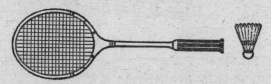

184 In bridge, when does a player become *dummy*?

The world of nature

185 How does a kangaroo carry its young?

186 How does the koala carry its young after the cub is about six months old?

187 What can amphibians do that fish cannot?

188 What have vertebrates got that invertebrates have not?

189 The dormouse fell asleep in the tea party in *Alice in Wonderland*. In what way is he a sleepy animal?

190 In what way does the hare act as if he were mad in March?

191 What is a cuckoo-pint?

192 What is cuckoo-spit?

193 What is a rodent?

194 What is a marsupial?

195 What is a mammal?

196 What is the only mammal that can fly?

197 Besides its duckbill, what is the unusual characteristic of the platypus?

198 What is remarkable about the migration of Scandinavian lemmings?

199 When the halibut lies on the sea-bed, which side is uppermost – the white or brown – and why?

200 Where does the giraffe live, and why does it find its long neck useful?

201 In what special way could Linnaeus be said to be a 'family man'?

202 In what way was Mendel a 'family man'?

203 Why is the bittern sometimes called the 'invisible bird'?

204 Why is the mandarin duck well-named?

General knowledge 4

205 Who was the English outlaw who led the Merry Men?
206 Who was the king of the Knights of the Round Table?
207 What is *anthracite*?
208 What is a *Bedouin*?
209 What kind of bicycle is a *tandem*?
210 If you rode pillion, where would you be?
211 Why is Kuwait such a wealthy country?
212 Why is the River Rhine so important to the commerce of Europe?
213 What is the colour of demerara sugar?
214 What is the usual colour of platinum?
215 What used to happen when the curfew sounded?
216 When does reveille sound?
217 What is the symbol used by the Egg Marketing Board?
218 What symbol is used on road signs to indicate a school?
219 What was the common interest of Samuel Pepys and John Evelyn?
220 What was the *Water Ordeal* to which women accused of being witches were subjected?
221 Why is Mary Arden's house at Wilmcote, Warwickshire, a tourist attraction?
222 Who was the architect of Coventry Cathedral, and who designed the famous tapestry?
223 Who wrote the pamphlet *Post Office Reform* in 1837, and why is it important?
224 Who wrote in 1859 *On the Origin of the Species by Natural Selection*, and why is it an important document?

Far-away places

225 What is this ship?

226 Where are the Victoria Falls?

227 What famous explorer gave the Victoria Falls their name?

228 In which mountain range is Mount Everest?

229 In which mountain range is the Matterhorn?

230 Where is the Sargasso Sea, and what is it particularly noted for?

231 Where is the Dogger Bank, and what does it mainly consist of?

232 In which hills does the River Mersey have its source?

233 In which hills does the River Thames have its source?

234 What famous mountain is considered sacred by some Japanese?

235 What famous mountain overlooks Cape Town, in South Africa?

236 In which country is Kilimanjaro?

237 In which country is Popocatepetl?

238 Where is the Black Country?

239 Where is the Wash?

240 What is the capital of Indonesia?

241 What is the capital of Malaysia?

242 From what mountain range does the wind known as the *chinook* blow?

Speed quiz 3 – animals

How many can you get right in TWO minutes?

243   What do we call a female fox?
244   What do we call a male rabbit?
245   Is the whale a mammal or a fish?
246   Is the bat a mammal or a bird?
247   Does the polar bear live in the Arctic or Antarctic region?
248   Does the penguin live in the Arctic or Antarctic region?
249   Besides their speed, what other form of natural defence do many deer possess?
250   What form of natural defence do wild boar possess?
251   What creatures live in an aviary?
252   What birds live in an eyrie?
253   What are these creatures and where do they live?

254   What is the American bison usually called?
255   In which continent do we find the coyote?
256   In which continent is the wild dog known as the dingo found?
257   What animal lives in a drey?
258   What animal lives in a lodge?
259   What is the home of the badger called?
260   What is the home of the hare called?
261   What creatures live in an apiary?
262   What creatures live in a formicary?

General knowledge 5

263 Why did the Egyptians build such big and splendid pyramids?

264 Why was an invitation to perform at the Roman Colosseum not always welcomed?

265 What are pussy willows, and how do they get this name?

266 What is a Lady's Smock, and where will you find it?

267 What is the main difference between Premium Bonds and National Savings Certificates?

268 What is the main differences between the use of crossed and open cheques?

269 Our copper coins are not pure copper; what are they made of?

270 Our silver coins are no longer made of silver; what are they made of?

271 What is a waterspout?

272 What is a dust devil?

273 Why was the Duke of Marlborough's house given the name of Blenheim?

274 Why is a division of Lincolnshire known as Holland?

275 What information does a meteorologist get from a seismometer?

276 What information does a pilot get from his altimeter?

277 What was the Siege of Sidney Street?

278 What is the American *whistle-stop tour*?

279 What was the American *showboat*?

280 What is a *son et lumière*?

281 What is a *paradox*?

282 What is a *mixed metaphor*?

People of long ago 1

283 Who was the general of ancient Carthage, and why is his name linked with war elephants?

284 Who was the young prince of Macedonia who became the first world conqueror, and what was special about his horse Bucephalus?

285 Who became king twice, first as the Sixth and then as the First?

286 Who was Lord Protector of the Commonwealth when England had no king?

287 Traditionally, how did Blondel discover where his master, Richard Coeur-de-Lion, was imprisoned?

288 Traditionally, what was Nell Gwyn's job when the Merry Monarch first saw her?

289 Who was the general who invaded Britain in 55 B.C., and what is the story behind the standar-bearer of the Tenth Legion?

290 Who was the prince who fought at the Battle of Crécy and how did he win his spurs?

291 Whom did King Henry III of England acknowledge as Prince of Wales?

292 Who was known as the Hammer of the Scots?

293 What invention do we associate with Richard Arkwright?

294 What reform do we associate with William Wilberforce?

295 Who was the commander of the Greek army which fought against Troy?

296 Who was the wife of Ulysses?

297 Why was General Gordon known as 'Chinese Gordon' and for what historic incident is he better known?

298 In World War I politics, who was known as the Welsh Wizard?

Team quiz 3

London

299a Where is the statue commonly known as Eros?

300a What does the Cenotaph commemorate, and what does the word *cenotaph* mean?

301a Where and what is Cleopatra's needle?

302a Where would you go to see a copy of the Domesday Book?

Bridges

303a What is a *drawbridge*?

304a What is an *aqueduct*?

305a The new Severn Bridge is a suspension bridge. What is a *suspension bridge*?

306a What bridge is associated with Shakespeare's Shylock and where does it stand?

Money

307a In which country are *pesetas* the currency?

308a What is *counterfeit money*?

309a What does a *teller* in a bank do?

310a What do we mean by the *sterling area*?

London

299b Where is Nelson's Column?

300b What does the Monument commemorate, and why is it exactly 202 feet tall?

301b Where and what is Speaker's Corner?

302b Where would you go to see a collection of the possessions of the Duke of Wellington?

Bridges

303b What is a *swing bridge*?

304b What is a *pontoon bridge*?

305b London's Tower Bridge is a bascule bridge; what is a *bascule bridge*?

306b Where is the Bridge of Sighs, and why is it so called?

Money

307b In which country are *lire* the currency?

308b What is known as *blood money*?

309b What does a *usurer* do?

310b What is *specie*?

311 Who or what is a *gate-crasher*?

312 Who or what is a *bulldozer*?

313 There are many tors on Dartmoor, such as Hay Tor and King Tor. What is a *tor*?

314 What does the *ben* in Scottish place-names stand for?

315 In which country is the world's biggest gold mine?

316 Where does the United States keep its gold?

317 What would you expect to get out of a decanter?

318 What would you expect to get out of a hydrant?

319 What language do the people of Chile speak?

320 What language do the people of Brazil speak?

321 What is the difference between meteors and meteorites?

322 What is the difference between icebergs and ice-floes?

323 What is *stamp duty*?

324 What is an *arabesque* in ballet?

325 Why do ships have stabilizers, and how do they work?

326 What is the difference between a church and a cathedral?

327 What is the difference between a knight and a baronet?

328 What are the names of these architectural styles?

Speed quiz 4

How many can you get right in TWO minutes?

Gods

329 Who was the Roman god of war? *Mars*
330 Who was the god of the sea? *Neptune*
331 Who was the father of the gods? *Jupiter (Zeus)*
332 Who was the mother of the gods? *Juno, Hera*
333 Who was the messenger of the gods? *Mercury, Hermes*
334 In Roman mythology, who was the huntress? *Diana*
335 Who was the god of wine and revelry? *Bacchus*
336 Who was the goddess of wisdom? *Minerva, Athena*

Cities

337 In which countries are the following large cities?
  (i)   Tokyo   (ii)   Chicago
  (iii) Leningrad   (iv)   Peking
  (v)   Cairo   (vi)   Bombay
  (vii) Havana   (viii) Djakarta

Partners

338 If a duke should partner a duchess, who should partner a witch?
339 If a wife should partner a husband, who should partner a Red Indian brave?
340 Who should partner a sultan?
341 Who should partner a marquis?
342 What is the masculine equivalent of a mare?
343 What is the feminine equivalent of a fox?
344 In Shakespeare's *Hamlet*, when Claudius was king of Denmark who was his queen?

The Bard of Avon

---

345 In which Shakespeare play do Brutus and Cassius, with other conspirators, assassinate a Roman dictator?

346 In which Shakespeare play does a Scottish thane assassinate his king?

347 In *The Taming of the Shrew*, how does Petruchio teach his wife a lesson?

348 How does Portia teach Shylock a lesson in *The Merchant of Venice*?

349 In *The Merchant of Venice*, of what metal is the casket that has this inscription: 'Who chooseth me shall get as much as he deserves'?

350 And what casket does Bassanio choose?

351 How does Prince Hal treat his 'fat friend' Sir John Falstaff when he becomes King Henry V?

352 How does Richard III show his appreciation of all the help he gets from the Duke of Buckingham to gain the throne?

353 Which of Shakespeare's plays begins with the following words and who speaks them?
'If music be the food of love, play on,
Give me excess of it . . .'

354 Which play ends with the following words, and who speaks them?
'So, good night unto you all.
Give me your hands, if we be friends,
And Robin shall restore amends.'

355 In which of Shakespeare's plays does a king's ghost appear on the ramparts of a castle?

356 In which play is there a sleep-walking scene?

357 Who is Malvolio, and in which play does he appear?

358 Who is Caliban, and in which play does he appear?

359 What were the names of King Lear's three daughters?

360 What were the three prophecies that the witches forecast
to Macbeth upon the blasted heath?

361 The three witches make a further prophecy, that:
'Macbeth shall never vanquished be, until
Great Birnam wood to high Dunsinane hill
Shall come against him.'
How is this prophecy realized?

362 Name three of the yokels who acted *Pyramus and
Thisbe* in *A Midsummer Night's Dream*.

363 In *Twelfth Night*, what did Malvolio wear, as he thought,
to please Olivia?

364 In which of Shakespeare's plays is a tragedy forecast
by the following omens:
'A lioness hath whelped in the streets
And graves have yawned and yielded up their dead'?

365 In which play is Queen Mab's chariot described as:
'. . . an empty hazel-nut,
Made by the joiner squirrel or old grub,
Time out o' mind the fairies' coachmakers.
And in this state she gallops night by night
Through lovers' brains, and then they dream of love . . .'?

366 Which play does this scene suggest?

Team quiz 4 – far-away places

Rivers and Towns

On what rivers are the following towns (each pair of towns is on the same river)?

367a Bonn and Cologne?
368a Quebec and Montreal?
369a Arles and Lyon?
370a Matadi and Léopoldville?

Regions and Areas

The following are regions or areas. Firstly, where are they? And secondly, what sort of country are they?

371a The Broads?
372a The Pampas?
373a The fjords?
374a The Polders?

Japan

375a What name do the Japanese give to their country?
376a What is the name of the long robe that the Japanese girls wear?
377a What is the special reason that the Japanese grow mulberry trees in vast numbers?
378a What is a *jinriksha*? (This is more commonly known as a *rickshaw*.)

Rivers and towns

On what rivers are the following pairs of towns?
367b Paris and Rouen?
368b Budapest and Belgrade?
369b Luxor and Wadi Halfa?
370b Patna and Calcutta?

Regions and areas

The following are regions and areas. Firstly, where are
they? And secondly, what sort of country are they?
371b The Downs?
372b The Rockies?
373b The Himalayas?
374b The Tundra?

Japan

375b Which is the highest mountain in Japan?
376b What is the name given to girls in Japan who act as
hostesses?
377b What is the staple food in Japan?
378b What is *ju-jitsu*? (This is sometimes known as *judo*).

The world of science

379 Why is it dangerous to put a hot test tube in cold water to cool it?

380 What is a bunsen burner and how does it work?

381 What happens when red litmus paper is put into an alkaline solution?

382 Why is aluminium foil put between the walls and under the roof of some houses when central heating is installed?

383 Why do electricians sometimes wear rubber gloves?

384 Why do firemen have asbestos clothing?

385 Who was the professor of mathematics who, in the sixteenth century, dropped two weights from a leaning tower, and what was he setting out to prove?

386 Why could the equation $E = mc^2$ be thought of as the best symbol of Einstein's achievement?

387 Some spectacles have bi-focal lenses. What are these and what are they for?

388 What is a contact lens?

389 Why is calor gas especially suitable as a fuel for caravans and campers?

390 Why is an alcohol thermometer used for measuring low temperatures rather than a mercury one?

391 How does a vacuum cleaner work?

392 How does a vacuum flask work?

393 What is the difference between *fission* and *fusion* in producing atomic energy.

394 How does a *diode* thermionic valve differ from a *triode*?

395 What is the connection between a great French scientist and a little boy from Alsace bitten by a mad dog?

396 What is the connection between a husband and wife team of scientists and several tons of pitchblende and a laboratory in Paris?

397 What is a *chorister*?

398 What is a *page-boy*?

399 How many days are there in a leap year?

400 How often does a leap year occur?

401 What is a ring master?

402 What is a toast master?

403 What do we mean when we say that a person is 'two-faced'?

404 What do we mean when we say that a person is 'poker-faced'?

405 What is the basic unit of money in France?

406 What is the basic unit of money in Germany?

407 What is the taste of sodium chloride?

408 Where would you see these soldiers and what is the name given to them?

409 How do scientists know what prehistoric animals looked like?

410 In motor cars, how does independent suspension help to give greater comfort?

411 How is the 'night safe' of a bank used?

412 What is the 'safe deposit' service that some banks provide?

413 What is a customs' union?

414 What are traveller's cheques?

415 What is Unesco?

416 What is Eldo?

Team quiz 5

Famous ships

417a Who was the famous explorer who sailed in the *Santa María*?
418a What are the names of the two ships known as the 'Queens' that went out of service as ocean liners in the late 1960s?
419a What kind of ship was the *Cutty Sark*?
420a How was the *Lusitania* sunk in 1915?

Hats

421a Who would be the most likely person to wear a bearskin?
422a Who were the first people to wear ten-gallon hats?
423a What is a fez, and what people is it associated with?
424a Who might be expected to wear a mortarboard, and what is it?

Occupations

425a What does a lumberjack do?
426a What is a steeplejack?
427a What does a contortionist do?
428a What is the difference between an astonomer and an astrologer?

What would you be if you . . .
429a . . . tricked a gamekeeper by snaring livestock on his estate?
430a . . . designed buildings?
431a . . . presided at an inquest?
432a . . . helped a surgeon by making your patients lose consciousness before an operation?

Famous ships

417b Who sailed in the *Mayflower*?

418b What were the two names of Francis Drake's ship which sailed round the world?

419b What kind of ship was the *Nautilus*?

420b How was the *Titanic* sunk?

Hats

421b Who is the most likely person to wear a sou'wester?

422b Who were the first people to wear tam-o'-shanters?

423b Describe a turban. What people wear it today?

424b Who might be expected to wear a mitre, and what is it?

Occupation

425b What does a dietician do?

426b What does a frogman do?

427b What does a statistician do?

428b What is the difference between an archaeologist and an anthropologist?

What would you be if you . . .

429b . . . cured animals of their injuries and ailments?

430b . . . made and sold spectacles?

431b . . . were the minister permanently representing your country at a foreign court or in a foreign state?

432b . . . helped patients get back the full use of their limbs by exercises and other forms of treatment?

The Bible

433 What were the names of the sons of Adam?

434 What were the names of Jacob's two wives?

435 Who was the king who tried to get the child Jesus killed?

436 Who was the son of Elizabeth and Zacharias who foretold Christ's coming?

437 Who were the three Magi who followed the star?

438 What were the presents that the Magi gave to the infant Christ?

439 Why did Cain kill his brother?

440 Why did Lot's wife turn into a pillar of salt?

441 Who was the leader who delivered a nation out of slavery in Egypt, and how was he concerned with tablets of stone on Mount Sinai?

442 What happened to Saint Paul on the road to Damascus?

443 Who was the giant that David killed, and how did he do it?

444 Whom did Delilah betray, and how did she do it?

445 Who said these words, and to whom: 'Fear not: for behold, I bring you good tidings of great joy, which shall be to all people'?

446 Who said these words, and to whom: 'Go ye into all the world, and preach the gospel to every creature'?

447 What did the Four Horsemen of the Apocalypse represent?

448 At the end of Peter's sermon on the day of Pentecost, three thousand souls joined the Church and they 'continued steadfastly' in four things. What were these things?

449 What do we mean by the *scale* of a map?

450 What are the *contour* lines on a map?

451 What is a *chiff-chaff*?

452 What is a *cheetah*?

453 What are these monuments and where will you see them?

454 Why were the Crusades known as the Holy Wars?

455 What is the name given to a fox's tail?

456 What kind of dog is a pointer, and why has it been given this name?

457 What is the technical name for your windpipe?

458 What is the technical name for your voice box?

459 What was the country known as Cathay?

460 Where was Phoenicia?

461 What kind of weather does an anti-cyclone usually bring in summer?

462 What kind of weather does the south-west or summer monsoon bring in India?

463 Give the order in which the River Rhine passes these towns: Düsseldorf, Strasbourg and Cologne.

464 Give the order in which the River Danube passes these towns: Budapest, Belgrade and Vienna.

465 What is a *limerick*?

466 What is an *elegy*?

467 What is a *crustacean*?

468 What kind of mammal is a *cetacean*?

Novels and poems

469 What is the title of the book that Robert Louis Stevenson wrote as a sequel to *Kidnapped*?

470 What famous novel has the subtitle 'A Romance of Exmoor'?

471 Which poem opens with the following words, and who wrote it?

'On Linden, when the sun was low,
All bloodless lay the untrodden snow,
And dark as winter was the flow
  Of Iser, rolling rapidly.'

472 Which poem begins with the following words and who wrote it?

'On either side the river lie
Long fields of barley and of rye,
That clothe the wold and meet the sky;
And thro' the field the road runs by
  To many-tower'd Camelot.'

473 In the story by Jules Verne, how long did Phineas Fogg take to go round the world?

474 In the stories by the Baroness Orczy, what symbol did Sir Percy Blakeney adopt to hide his identity?

475 What was the flower that Robert Burns called 'wee, modest, crimson-tipped flow'r'?

476 What were the flowers that William Wordsworth saw
'Beside the lake, beneath the trees,
Fluttering and dancing in the breeze'?

477 Writers have a way of creating their own magic places. Who was the author who created the land of Narnia?

478 Who created the Welsh fishing village under Milk Wood?

479 Loch Katrine, in Scotland, inspired an epic poem. What was the poem and who wrote it?

480 In which poem are these the first lines, and who wrote them?
'Oh, to be in England
Now that April's there . . .'

481 In the play by Sophocles, how did Antigone defy her uncle?

482 What are these and in what book do they appear?

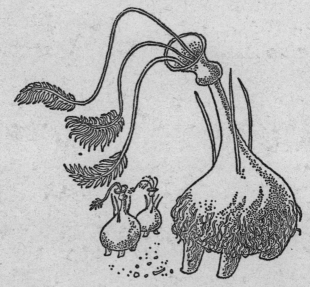

483 In which poem is this the first line, and who was the poet? 'Season of mists and mellow fruitfulness.'

484 What was the profession of Kingsley Amis's 'Lucky Jim'?

Speed quiz 5 – far-away places

How many can you get right in TWO minutes?

485 What is the capital of Sweden?

486 What is the capital of Hungary?

487 To what country does the island of Majorca belong?

488 To what country does Greenland belong?

489 Into what sea does the River Rhine flow?

490 What does the River Seine flow into?

491 What is Wagga Wagga, and where is it?

492 Where is this statue and what is its name?

493 Where are the Mendip Hills?

494 Where is Vesuvius?

495 Where is Mount Olympus?

496 Where is Parnassus?

497 Where is the Mount of Olives?

498 Where is Mount Ararat?

499 Where is the Côte d'Azur?

500 Where is the Costa Brava?

501 What is the Dutch port linked with Harwich?

502 What is the French port usually linked with Newhaven?

503 Is Cambodia north or south of the equator?

504 Are the Philippines north or south of the equator?

Sports and games 2

505 In what sport do we get the *butterfly* and the *crawl*?
506 In what sport do we get *maidens* and *wides*?
507 In show-jumping, what is a *pyramid fence*?
508 In tennis, what is a *double fault*?
509 What is *skin diving*?
510 Name the British woman rally driver who is married to a Swede.
511 How many games must be won for a set in tennis, and why does this number vary?
512 In cricket, what is the difference between the umpire's signal for a 4 boundary, and the signal to show that a boundary line has been cleared for a 6?
513 What is a *point-to-point* meeting in horse racing?
514 What is a motor-cycle scramble?
515 How many men in a Rubgy League team?
516 How many men in a Rugby Union team?
517 What is the significance of the *All-Blacks* in rugby football?
518 What is the significance of the yellow jersey in the Tour de France cycle race?
519 In what game is a *puck* used instead of a ball?
520 In tennis, what does a player have to do to win a game after *deuce* is called?
521 What was the first British football club to win the European Cup?
522 What is the Swaythling Cup awarded for?
523 Who won the first professional tennis tournament held at Wimbledon?
524 Who was the first runner to break the 'magic' four-minute mile?

Literature

525   Lilliput was the country of dwarfs in *Gulliver's Travels*, but what was the name of the country of giants?

526   Who is Biggles?

527   Who is Fagin?

528   Name the three castaways on the coral island, in the novel of that name.

529   In *Pilgrim's Progress* by John Bunyan, what are the names of the cities where the story begins and ends?

530   What did Shylock demand of the Merchant of Venice, if he could not meet his debts?

531   How much did the three jolly farmers of Walter de la Mare's poem stake against each other in their efforts to dance each other off the ground?

532   In *A Christmas Carol* by Charles Dickens, who was the partner of Jacob Marley?

533   In *Nicholas Nickleby,* who was the headmaster of Dotheboys Hall?

534   In one of Grimm's Fairy Tales, which has been turned into an opera, a boy and his sister are trapped by a witch in a house fenced in with gingerbread boys and girls. Who were the brother and sister, and how do the children escape?

535   In the story of *Peer Gynt*, the country lad is attacked by trolls in the hall of the mountain king. What makes them break off this attack?

536   Who wrote about *Moby Dick* and *Captain Ahab*?

537   Who wrote about *Doctor Dolittle* and his animals?

538   Who wrote:
'Nowhere and under no circumstances should a woman ever be quite accurate about her age'?

Speed quiz 6

How many can you get right in TWO minutes?

539 What do you get from a *box office*?
540 What is a *spinney*?
541 What is a *cloak-and-dagger* story?
542 What is a *Western*?
543 Where are the Scilly Isles?
544 Where are the Shetland Isles?
545 What was the ship in which the Pilgrim Fathers set sail for America?
546 What was the name of Columbus's ship used for his first Atlantic expedition?
547 What station is the London terminus of the *Royal Scot*?
548 What London station is the terminus for the *Red Dragon* train from Cardiff?
549 Where is Monte Carlo?
550 What is the aeroplane that is an Anglo-French project?
551 What would you expect a *clairvoyant* to tell you?
552 What would you expect to get from a *librettist*?
553 What was the title of the Russian monarch before the Revolution?
554 What is an *articulated* lorry?
555 In which English county does the Floral Dance take place each year?
556 With which English city is the Lambeth Walk associated?
557 Where did the Canterbury Pilgrims meet to begin their journey?
558 In what Fleet Street coffee house did Samuel Johnson and his group meet?

559 What is the connection between Little Miss Muffet of the nursery rhyme and Robert the Bruce of Scotland?

560 What is the connection between William Tell, the Swiss hero, and Isaac Newton, the scientist?

561 If you were suffering from *mal de mer* where would you be?

562 If, in France, you used the *chemin de fer*, what would you be doing?

563 What causes tides in the seas and oceans?

564 Why is the sea salty?

565 What would something called a *clover leaf* mean to a motorist?

566 What might something called a *wind sock* mean to a pilot?

567 Who was the Dauphin?

568 Who is the Infanta?

569 What do we call these hats?

a   b   c   d

570 What is a *mackerel* sky?

571 What is a ship's *underwriter*?

572 What is a motor-car's *over-rider*?

573 Where is Longarone, and what was its tragedy in 1963?

574 Where is Skopje, and what was its tragedy in 1963?

575 What would you be concerned with if you were a member of the Howard League?

576 What would you be concerned with if you were a member of a Horological Society?

Work this one out

577   A garden has an area of 4,840 square yards. What is a better way of expressing this?

578   A snail moves 2.54 centimetres in half an hour. What is its speed in inches per hour?

579   A satellite can orbit the earth in less than 2 hours, but what trip takes 27 days, 7 hours, 43 minutes and 11.5 seconds?

580   It is 3,006 miles from London to New York City. What does 24,903 miles measure?

581   A clock that strikes the number of hours every hour takes eight seconds to strike 9 o'clock. How many seconds will it take to strike 12 o'clock?

582   In a test, John had 7 marks below the class average, Bill 8 marks above, and David got 75. The average of the three boys' marks was the same as the class average. How many marks did John and Bill get?

583   An angle of 90 degrees is known as a right angle. What do we call an angle of less than 90 degrees?

584   A hexagon is a six-sided figure. What name do we give to a five-sided figure?

585   A train travelling at 30 miles an hour takes four hours to reach its destination. It travels at an average speed of 20 miles an hour on the return journey. What is the average speed of the train for the double journey?

586   A man buys a second-hand motor-bike for £60. He does it up and sells it for £70. Later, he buys back the same bike for £40, and then makes a deal to sell it at £50. What was his profit or loss on the whole transaction?

Team quiz 6

Dates

587a Why is the fifth of November a special date?
588a What happened on 11 November 1918?
589a What special day of the year do the Druids celebrate at Stonehenge?
590a What event took place in France on 14 July 1789?

Why?

591a Why do winter campers sometimes wear string or mesh vests?
592a Why should motorists carry a fire extinguisher?
593a Why does a deep-sea diver wear boots with soles made of lead?
594a Why do we pickle some foods, such as onions?

The Theatre

595a What are the *wings* in a theatre?
596a What in the theatre is a *property master*?
597a What is an *apron stage*?
598a In what country is *kabuki* a form of drama?

Politics

599a What is a republic?
600a In an election, who are the constituents?
601a What is the Cabinet?
602a Of which country is the *Riksdag* the parliament?

Dates

587b   Why is the first of April a special date?

588b   What is celebrated on 8 May?

589b   What do Americans celebrate on the fourth Thursday of November?

590b   What event took place in America on 4 July 1776?

Why?

591b   Why do skiers wear dark glasses?

592b   Why should you never touch anything electrical when your hands are wet?

593b   Why does an astronaut wear magnets on his boots?

594b   Why are oranges a healthy food to eat?

The Theatre

595b   What are the *flies* in a theatre?

596b   What is a *stage manager* in the theatre?

597b   What is the *denouement* of a play?

598b   In what country is the *no* play a form of drama?

Politics

599b   What is a federation of states?

600b   In an election, what is a *canvasser*?

601b   What is *Hansard*?

602b   Of which country is the *Cortes* the parliament?

Speed quiz 7 – famous women

How many can you get right in TWO minutes?

603   Whose abduction caused a twenty years' war?
604   Which queen was the longest-reigning British monarch?
605   Who was the Queen of England when the Spanish Armada
      sailed against her country?
606   Who was King Henry VIII's last wife?
607   Who won the Gold Medal in the women's long jump at
      the Tokyo Olympic Games in 1964?
608   Who won the Gold Medal in the women's 800 metres at
      Tokyo?
609   Who wrote *Jane Eyre*?
610   Who wrote *Pride and Prejudice*?
611   Who was the girl who reigned as Queen of England
      for only nine days?
612   Who was the Queen of England who married a Spanish
      king?
613   According to legend, which queen killed herself by holding
      an asp?
614   In Virgil's *Aeneid*, who is the queen who kills herself
      when Aeneas leaves her?
615   In what art has Joan Sutherland achieved fame?
616   In what art has Beryl Grey achieved fame?
617   In what art has Maria Callas achieved fame?
618   In what art has Edith Sitwell achieved fame?
619   What was the pen-name of Mary Ann Evans, who wrote
      Silas Marner?
620   What was the pen-name of Baroness Dudevant, the
      French novelist who wrote *Indiana*?
621   In what art has Barbara Hepworth achieved fame?
622   In what art has Elizabeth Lutyens achieved fame?

623 What kind of ceremonies were performed over the anvil at Gretna Green?

624 What could you expect to see on a summer's day at Lords, in London?

625 Where would a *snorkel* be used?

626 Where might an *iron lung* be used?

627 Where would you be if you were on a *footplate*?

628 Where would you be if you were standing on a *companion-way*?

629 Why might Dick Turpin have shuddered at the thought of Tyburn Tree?

630 Why did no one get a cup of tea at the Boston Tea Party?

631 What does *tacking* mean to yachtsmen?

632 How does a yachtsman 'trim' the sails?

633 You may have seen grotesque *gargoyles* on some buildings. What is their purpose?

634 You might live in a *mews* today, but what were these buildings used for before London was short of living space?

635 What happens at an ordination ceremony?

636 What happens at an investiture at court?

637 Why was a statue of Robert Stephenson erected in Euston Square?

638 In a competition in 1829 were *Novelty*, *Rocket*, *Perseverance* and *Sanspareil*. What were they, and who won?

639 What was the name given to the followers of Brigadier Charles Orde Wingate, and what did they set out to do?

640 Who were the two Victorian politicians who were known as 'the People's Tribune' and 'Dizzy', and which one was the Liberal and which the Conservative?

People of long ago 2

---

641 Who was the warrior queen who fought against the Romans in ancient Britain?

642 Who was the English king who won the battle of Agincourt?

643 Who was the first king to reign over both Scotland and England?

644 Who was the first man to set up a printing press in England?

645 In a Roman 'triumph', what did the general wear on his head as a sign of honour?

646 In the days of ancient Rome, what was the galley slave condemned to?

647 In the days of Queen Elizabeth I, what was the Babington plot?

648 What monarchs came directly before and after Elizabeth I?

649 Who was the English general who captured Quebec from the French in 1759?

650 Who was the Frenchman who was mainly responsible for the summoning of our first parliament?

651 Why was it that Columbus, who was an Italian, won the American empire for Spain?

652 Who was the Boer who fought against Great Britain in the Boer War, and yet became prime minister of the Union of South Africa?

653 Two of Britain's prime ministers were father and son. Who were they?

654 Two of Queen Victoria's uncles were kings of Great Britain. Who were they?

655 What relation was James VI of Scotland (James I of England) to Mary, Queen of Scots, and to Queen Elizabeth?

656 During the nineteenth century, there was a Prince
Regent and a Prince Consort. Who were they, and why
did they have different titles?

657 By what title is Arthur Wellesley better known?

658 John Churchill was one of Britain's greatest
generals. By what title is he better known?

659 Who in 1526 gave Hampton Court to whom?

660 What is the island off the Scottish coast which is
associated with St. Columba, and why?

661 Who sailed in this
ship, what was its
name, and what
did he do in it?

662 Who sailed in
this ship, what
was its name, and
what did he do
in it?

663 Marryat created Midshipman Easy; who created Midshipman Horatio Hornblower?

664 Fleming created James Bond; who created Richard Hannay?

665 What is a *milking parlour*?

666 What is an *oast house*?

667 What kind of snake is this and what is it doing?

668 In what kind of entertainment does the *choreographer* play a part, and what does he do?

669 Where would you find the Crown Jewels?

670 Where is Poet's Corner?

671 What is a *monorail* railway?

672 What is a *conchologist*?

673 Who would be most likely to use a *metronome*?

674 Who would be most likely to use a *chronometer*?

675 What is the sacred river of the Hindus?

676 What country is sometimes called the *Roof of the World*?

677 What is the *Koran*?

678 Why is Cape Kennedy important in the story of exploration?

679 How did Benjamin Franklin show that a lightning flash was really a gigantic electric spark?

680 What happens when an aeroplane breaks the sound barrier?

681 Who wrote the poem *The Dream of Gerontius*, and who composed the music for it?

682 Who is the composer of the music entitled 'The Planets'?

Famous characters

683 What was the first sign that Robinson Crusoe had of
     another inhabitant on his island?

684 How did Aladdin make the genie appear when he wanted
     him?

685 How did Rider Haggard's 'She' keep her eternal youth?

686 From whom do Pip's 'Great Expectations' come in the
     Dickens novel with that title?

687 In which street did Sherlock Holmes live?

688 Who was Sherlock Holmes's assistant?

689 Where was Leontes' palace in Shakespeare's *The Winter's
     Tale*?

690 What was the name of Rochester's home in *Jane Eyre*?

691 In which book do we get a rabbit who exclaims 'By me
     ears and whiskers I shall be late'?

692 In which book do we get a parrot who screams 'Pieces of
     Eight! Pieces of Eight!'?

693 Who is the magician in the tales of King Arthur, and who
     is King Arthur's fairy sister?

694 In a long poem by Samuel Taylor Coleridge, the killing
     of an albatross brings ill-luck to a ship. (i) Who kills the
     albatross? (This gives you the title of the poem.) (ii) How
     do the sailors show their displeasure at the act?

695 What are the names of the 'Little Women' in the book by
     Louisa M. Alcott?

696 Who are the 'Three Musketeers' and who is their boon
     companion in the book by Alexander Dumas?

697 Who was Don Quixote, and who wrote about him?

698 Who was Huckleberry Finn, and who wrote about him?

699 Who wrote a book about a man named Mr. Polly?

700 In the book *Portrait of the Artist as a Young Man*,
     who was the 'artist'?

Answers

General knowledge 1

1 An heirloom is a piece of personal property that has been
   in a family for generations, such as a piece of jewellery
   or furniture.

2 A spinet is a musical instrument of the harpsichord
   family. It was used in the seventeenth and eighteenth
   centuries.

3 A microbe is an extremely tiny living thing – plant or
   animal. The term is particularly used of bacteria causing
   disease or fermentation.

4 *a* Micrometer, used for measuring minute distances or
   angles. *b* Metronome, which can be set to beat so many
   times a minute, and so give the right speed of performance
   for a piece of music. *c* Anemometer, for gauging the
   speed of the wind.

5 It is a surface burn in which the skin is red and painful
   but not broken or blistered. *Second degree* burns have
   blisters, and *third degree burns* involve destruction of
   skin and tissue. More serious burns are classified further,
   up to a *sixth degree burn* which involves tissues burnt to
   the bone.

6 A partly broken or bent bone.

7 He had a tapestry made which showed scenes from the
   invasion. This became known as the Bayeux Tapestry.
   According to tradition, William's wife, Matilda,
   embroidered it for his half-brother, Odo, the Bishop of
   Bayeux. It was certainly designed immediately after the
   invasion, when Odo was the Bishop of Bayeux, and it was
   included in an inventory of the decorations and ornaments
   of the cathedral in 1476. But it was more probably
   executed by Norman craftsmen for the bishop.

8 He had a survey carried out which was recorded in the Domesday Book. The survey was carried out in 1086 and recorded in two volumes. The name 'Domesday Book' was given to the records in the twelfth century.

9 A jaywalker is a pedestrian who is careless in his use of the roads and his attitude to traffic and traffic regulations.

10 A road hog is a reckless or inconsiderate motorist or cyclist who selfishly obstructs other road users.

11 Science, from the Latin *scire*.

12 *Geo* stands for the *earth*. It comes from the Greek word *geo*, meaning earth.

13 The bora.

14 The sirocco.

15 Laughing gas.

16 Dry ice.

17 An ecologist studies the relations of living organisms (plants, animals, or peoples) to their environment. The study is called *ecology*.

18 Fossils. The study of fossils is called *palaeontology*.

Authors and their works

19 Harriet Beecher Stowe.

20 Thomas Hughes.

21 It was a ship – in distress. The ship's name was *The Cape Wrath*.

22 An otter. The novel is called *Tarka the Otter*.

23 George Orwell (real name Eric Blair). The farm animals revolt against their human masters, who are eventually replaced by other dictators – the pigs. It is a satire on Communism.

24 Rudyard Kipling.

25 Children enjoying outdoor activities. Ransome's books are mainly about camping and sailing.

26 Secret Service adventures. Johns's books are full of flying,
    action and adventure. The main character is Biggles, the
    pilot, who flies all over the world to unravel plots.

27 It was a prisoner-of-war camp in a German fortress,
    Colditz Castle. Reid's novel was called *The Colditz Story*.

28 Cranford was the name of a Cheshire village in a novel
    by that name. It was based in part on Knutsford, which
    at one time was Mrs Gaskell's home.

29 Robert Bolt wrote the play about Sir Thomas More.
    Paul Scofield played the leading role in both the London
    production of the play and the film made from it.

30 The 'beloved country' is South Africa, where the author,
    Alan Paton, was born. It is the story of a Zulu minister
    and his children.

31 The poet was John Milton. In *Paradise Lost*, Satan
    is driven out of heaven, and in *Paradise Regained* he is
    finally vanquished.

32 Homer, in the *Iliad*. In it, he tells of the events leading
    up to the death of Hector in the Siege of Troy. The
    central theme of the *Iliad* is Achilles' quarrel with
    Agamemnon. (According to tradition, Homer was blind,
    but there is no evidence that he was when he wrote his
    great works, the *Iliad* and the *Odyssey*. Little is known for
    certain about Homer, and it is not even certain that he
    wrote the works that bear his name.)

33 Jack London wrote the novel about White Fang, a dog.
    The dog came out of the wilds to live with man.

34 John Wyndham wrote *The Midwich Cuckoos*, a science
    fiction novel. A power from outer space causes a number
    of children with similar characteristics to be born in
    Midwich, a village in Britain. The children are
    precocious and have the unusual facility of simultaneous
    learning, i.e. if one child learns something the identical
    knowledge is acquired by all the others. They become
    ruthless and potentially dangerous to mankind, and are

finally annihilated by a man who sacrifices his own life
in the act. The book was made into a film called *Village
of the Damned*.

35 Henrik Ibsen, a Norwegian.
36 Richard Brinsley Sheridan.
37 Lord Snow (C. P. Snow).
38 T. S. Eliot.

Speed quiz 1

39 Soldiers (and their families).
40 Monks or nuns.
41 Union of Soviet Socialist Republics (USSR).
42 Chinese People's Republic.
43 Portugal is a republic.
44 Denmark is a kingdom – one of the oldest in the world.
45 Joseph.
46 Daniel.
47 African natives, such as Zulus. A kraal is a collection of
    huts that make up the village, usually surrounded by a
    stockade. Kraals are found in southern or central Africa.
48 Red Indians, especially the Sioux and Dakota Indians.
    A tepee is a cone-shaped tent, better known as a wigwam.
49 Canals (James Brindley).
50 Railways (Isambard Kingdom Brunel).
51 Lead.
52 Gold.
53 A dried plum.
54 A dried grape.
55 A Plantagenet.
56 York.
57 Godiva.
58 The wife of Othello.

Team quiz 1

59a Wednesday's child is full of woe. The rhyme goes:
'Monday's child is fair of face,
Tuesday's child is full of grace,
Wednesday's child is full of woe,
Thursday's child has far to go,
Friday's child is loving and giving,
Saturday's child works hard for its living,
And a child that is born on the Sabbath day
Is fair and wise and good and gay.'

59b Solomon Grundy was married on Wednesday.

60a Rain or dew might wet the ropes during the night. This would have the effect of tightening them, pulling the pegs out of the ground.

60b Caterpillars are a fruit pest. They develop from eggs laid by wingless female moths which crawl up the trunks of trees. The grease bands trap them.

61a Propellers, usually under the hovercraft, project it forwards on a cushion of air. The power is provided by a small jet engine fitted at the rear.

61b Deep-sea observation.

62a You must send a stamped, addressed (to yourself) envelope with your application.

62b The letters o.n.o. stand for 'or near offer'.

63a The hanging gardens were in Babylon and were a series of terraces planted with flowers, shrubs and trees. They were built by King Nebuchadnezzar II to make his bride from the mountains feel at home. Their wonder has been attributed to two things: either to the fact that they were artificially constructed in a desert city or to their beauty and their amazing construction.

63b The Zuider Zee is an ocean gulf off the Netherlands. It is being reclaimed from the sea to become farm land.

64a Cheese.

64b New Zealand (Canterbury is a province of New Zealand.)

65a The neap tide.

65b The Tropic of Capricorn.

66a Magistrates are addressed as 'Your Worships', although legal staff might call a magistrate 'sir'.

66b You address an ambassador as 'Your Excellency'.

67a Most ivory comes from the tusks of elephants. Some ivory is also obtained from walruses and other animals, such as rhinoceroses.

67b Ebony is hard, black wood.

68a A botanist studies plants.

68b An ornithologist studies birds.

69a A keystone gives an arch its strength. The arch would collapse without it. It is the brick or stone at the top of the arch, and is put in last. The keystone is so called because it is said to lock or 'key' the whole together.

69b Pectin helps to make jam 'jell'. It is a white substance found in most fruits.

70a A masque was a play without a story or a climax, but with long speeches. Masques were usually played at court and actors originally wore masks.

70b Barnstormers were actors or strolling players who gave performances whenever they could gather an audience, even in barns. The term was used, in the fourteenth century, to refer to theatre companies whose work was characterized by ranting and shouting and general violence in speech and gesture.

71a Oxy-acetylene welding is a method of joining two pieces of metal together with a blowlamp to give high temperatures. It is so called because *oxygen* and *acetylene* are mixed in the right quantities to obtain the heat required. With the blowlamp in one hand applied to the join, a welder places a slender rod of metal in the hot flame with his other hand. He stirs the molten metal between the edges of the metal to be joined.

71b A temporary stitch which is used in plain sewing to hold two pieces of material together and to guide permanent sewing.

72a Widdicombe Fair is in Devon and the old grey mare 'her took sick and died'.

72b Ilkley Moor is in Yorkshire. If you do not take the singer's advice, you'll die and 'worms will come and eat you up'.

73a The model is first completely constructed outside the bottle. The masts are then folded down, the ship slid down the bottle's neck, and the masts pulled up with a piece of cotton that can be pulled off.

73b When a grain of sand or other impurity gets between the shells, the oyster covers it with successive layers of a substance called *nacre*. Over a number of years, this forms a pearl.

74a The goat's skin. The leather was originally made by the Moors of Spain and Morocco.

74b The fur of the musk rat.

Music and song

75 '... With heart and soul and voice'.

76 '... The glorious song of old'.

77 The song is a sea shanty and would have been sung by a sailor.

78 The song is a Negro Spiritual and would most likely have been sung by a Negro.

79 Richard Rodgers wrote the music, and Oscar Hammerstein II the lyrics.

80 Frederick Loewe wrote the music, and Alan Jay Lerner the lyrics.

81 The composer was Bizet, the opera *Carmen*.

82 The composer was Gounod, and the opera *Faust*, which is also the name of the old man.

83 Pizzicato is the plucking of the strings with the fingers to get a special staccato effect.

84 Smoothly without breaks, performed with a smooth connection between the notes.

85 *Fidelio*, sometimes called *Die Eheliche Liebe*, which means *married love*.

86 There are four operas: *The Rhinegold* (Das Rheingold), *The Valkyrie* (Die Walküre), *Siegfried*, and *Dusk* (or *Twilight*) *of the Gods* (Götterdämmerung).

87 Tchaikovsky.

88 Rimsky-Korsakov.

89 Rossini. Semiramide was the princess of Babylon.

90 Wagner. Lohengrin, the mysterious knight who gives the opera its title, is a knight of the Holy Grail. As such, he guards the Holy Grail.

91 The composer was Smetana and the country Bohemia, or Czechoslovakia. On 20 October 1874, after he had begun the second symphonic poem ('Moldau' – a river in Bohemia), the composer went stone deaf in both ears.

92 The composer was Borodin, and Prince Igor was Russian.

93 *Fantastic Symphony* (or *Symphonie Fantastique*), by Berlioz. The inspiration was the unhappy love affair of Berlioz with Harriet Smithson.

94 *a* Serpent *b* French Horn *c* Saxophone *d* Tambourine.

General knowledge 2

95 Paintings (Tate Gallery).

96 A reconstruction of the solar system, showing the motions of the planets with projections on a domed ceiling of various celestial images and effects, such as the sky at night at a specific time and place.

97 A MiG is a Russian interceptor plane. It is a jet monoplane that is used for tactical purposes, generally as a fighter. It is named after Mikoyan and Gurevich who collaborated in the design.

98 An apple Charlotte is a kind of pudding made of stewed apples, with a covering of bread, biscuits, sponge-cake or breadcrumbs. (Not to be confused with apple crumble, which has a top of crumbled pastry.)

99 A wind rose is a diagram marking off the direction of the winds that blow in a place over a period. You can find out the prevailing winds.

100 An anemometer is an instrument for measuring the force of the wind. It gives the velocity of the wind.

101 It provides cheap overnight accommodation for its members. It is an international youth organization. The sleeping accommodation is usually in dormitories, with bed, blankets and mattress. Kitchens are always available for use, and sometimes meals are provided.

102 The National Trust owns, maintains or protects large areas of countryside and many monuments of Britain's historical heritage, such as Runnymede and part of Hadrian's Wall. For the hiker, the preservation of beautiful countryside, such as 80,000 acres in the Lake District, is most important. The National Trust is a charity financed by subscription (it is not a government department), and preserves about 300,000 acres of land altogether.

103 Because he founded the colony of Pennsylvania in America as a refuge from persecution for his fellow Quakers. He also founded Philadelphia, the largest city in the state of Pennsylvania.

104 Ariadne, the daughter of King Minos of Crete, gave Theseus a ball of thread which he unwound as he entered the maze-like Labyrinth. After he had killed the Minotaur, he used the thread to retrace his steps out of the maze.

105 The British Legion was formed for ex-service men and women. It now caters for all men and women who have served in the forces and drawn at least seven days' pay, men and women of the Red Cross and St. John Ambulance Association who have been attached to a military unit during hostilities, merchant seamen who have served during hostilities, and honorary members with the ideals of the Legion at heart.

106 They are usually known as Quakers, a term applied to the group in 1650 by Justice Gervase Bennett because George Fox, the founder of the movement, told him to 'tremble at the word of the Lord'.

107 Afrikaans is a language developed from Dutch, and used mainly by South Africans of Dutch origin. It is an official language of South Africa, along with English.

108 Esperanto is an artificial language, invented in 1887 by Lazarus Zamenhof, a Polish Jew. He was nicknamed 'Doktoro Esperanto' (the hoping doctor). In spite of competitors, this remains the world's foremost auxiliary language and has an increasing number of adherents, especially in Russia and China.

109 It is a group of schools designed to strengthen the character of youth through adventure. Boys from a wide range of backgrounds meet and work together. At the schools' courses they can learn seamanship, rock-climbing and canoeing, and take part in athletics and cross-country expeditions. There are mountain schools at Eskdale and Ullswater, sea schools at Aberdovey and Murray, and a moorland school in Devon, at Ashburton. A girl's school was opened in 1963 in Towyn, Merionethshire. The original Outward Bound school, in Aberdovey, was founded in 1941 by Kurt Hahn and Lawrence Durning Holt as a sea school for boys in the Merchant Navy.

110 It is an organization that arranges for volunteer university graduates, professionally qualified staff, school leavers, and apprentices to serve in countries overseas, mostly on educational projects but also on agricultural, building and medical projects. Board, lodging, pocket money and free medical attention are supplied by their hosts.

111 They were called the Suffragettes (suffrage meaning 'the vote'). They wanted the same voting rights as men had. In 1918 women over 30 were given the vote, and in 1928 the Suffragettes achieved their full object, the right to vote from the age of 21.

112 Sir Christopher Wren, who was the architect of St. Paul's Cathedral and more than fifty churches in the city, and of Temple Bar and the Monument.

Speed quiz 2

113 Tom, Tom, the piper's son.
114 The old woman who lived in a shoe.
115 Automobile Association.
116 G.P. stands for General Practitioner – a doctor in general practice.
117 Cash on delivery.
118 Royal Automobile Club (also Royal Armoured Corps).
119 China.
120 Dover.
121 Through its fangs.
122 Through its tongue.
123 You would probably be a teacher, because N.U.T. stands for the National Union of Teachers.
124 A doctor – B.M.A. stands for British Medical Association.
125 An architect's house – the letters stand for Fellow of the Royal Institue of British Architects.
126 A vet's house – the letters stand for Fellow of the Royal College of Veterinary Surgeons.
127 Very small distances.

128 Very small electric currents.

129 The spider. It was the spider's example that inspired Bruce to further efforts to liberate his country.

130 The elephant. Hannibal was the general who took his war elephants across the Alps.

131 Opium.

132 Quinine.

Team quiz 2 – words and sayings

133a A *colander* is a perforated vessel used as a strainer in cookery. A *calendar* is a table of the dates, days, weeks, and months of the year, sometimes indicating festivals and other special days. This is not to be confused with a *calender*, which is a press used in the manufacture of such materials as cloth or paper; another meaning is 'mendicant dervish'!

133b A *gorilla* is a type of large, powerful ape. A *guerilla* (also spelt *guerrilla*) is a man who takes part in irregular war usually as a member of a small group.

134a A *panacea* should be bound to cure housemaid's knee because, by definition, it is a universal remedy.

134b Because he could rest on it – a *misericord* is the shelving projection on the underside of a hinged seat in a choir stall, serving to support a person standing when the seat is turned up. Another meaning of *misericord* is a narrow-bladed dagger for killing a wounded foe, but a choir boy would hardly be in need of that unless his neighbour was singing out of tune.

135a (ii) A *drugget* is a coarse woollen shift used for a floor or table covering.

135b (ii) A *ptarmigan* is a bird of the grouse family that lives in the mountains.

136a Because it is a sum he must pay in addition to his rent. *Tithe* means *tenth*, and was the levy paid for the maintenance of religious establishments or for other church purposes.

136b Because it is only a nominal rent.

137a '. . . flock together'.

137b He catches the worm. 'It is the early bird that catches the worm' means that you have to be about your business early to get the best results.

138a Two in the bush. 'A bird in the hand is worth two in the bush' means that a certain possession is worth more than something of greater value that you only might be able to possess.

138b '. . . before they're hatched'. This means that you should not take action on the assumption that something is going to happen when there is a possibility that it may not turn out as you expected.

139a Let them lie. 'Let sleeping dogs lie' means that you should leave well alone.

139b The mice will play. 'When the cat's away the mice will play' means that people will take liberties when they are not being observed by someone in authority.

140a '. . . out of a sow's ear'. This means that you cannot make a good person out of someone who is basically rotten.

140b Fine birds. 'Fine feathers make fine birds' means that fine clothes make a person feel good and give other people a good impression.

141a (ii) Two colours (usually black and white) irregularly arranged.

141b (i) An officer aboard ship who keeps the accounts and usually has charge of the provisions.

142a (ii) A deep blue dye used to colour cotton and wool – it has a blue-violet colour.

142b (iii) A calendar.
143a (i) A man employed in loading ships.
143b (iii) A model of excellence.
144a (iii) A sleep-walker.
144b (ii) A rain gauge.

General knowledge 3

145 Aesop is famous for his fables, stories about animals to illustrate human faults and virtues.

146 Jacob and Ludwig Grimm wrote fairy tales. They were also philologists (specialists in language) and folklorists, and wrote books on both subjects.

147 A table that has one or more legs that can be opened or shut like a gate. The leg (or legs) supports the table top when opened. When closed, the table leaf shuts down and so the table takes up less space.

148 A door that consists of separate parts so that the top half can be opened while the bottom half remains shut.

149 Market gardening is the cultivation of flowers, soft fruits and vegetables for profit.

150 A stock market is an exchange where the shares in companies are bought and sold.

151 You would not be able to read or write.

152 You would be able to use two languages fluently.

153 That Joan Smith is a married woman whose name before she was married (maiden name) was Joan Brown. *Née* is French for *born*.

154 That John Smith is also known by an assumed name, John Brown. He might be a criminal wishing to conceal his identity.

155 It was a substance – which they never found – that would enable people to live forever. They also sought the *philosopher's stone* (also called elixir) that was considered essential to convert base metals into precious metals.

156 It was a legendary city or kingdom of enormous wealth that was supposed to lie somewhere in the Amazon Basin, in South America. It was sometimes talked of as 'the city of gold'.

157 In the days when letters and important documents were sealed with wax, a person pressed a seal into the wax. A *signet* is a private seal, and a signet ring was a finger ring with the seal set in it. This was a handy way of carrying a seal.

158 In the days when pens were plumes or feathers, they had to be regularly re-pointed. The knives used for this purpose were therefore called *pen* knives.

159 Jodrell Bank, Cheshire. It is a radio telescope that tracks bodies in the heavens.

160 A *hitch* is used to tie a rope to a ring, spar, post or similar object. A *splice* permanently joins the ends of two ropes, or forms a single rope into a permanent loop.

161 Over a door or window. A lintel is the horizontal piece of timber or stone above a door or window that supports the wall. The traditional materials for lintels of wood or stone are now being replaced by reinforced concrete or steel.

162 On a staircase. The newel post is the centre pillar of a winding stair – the steps wind around the newel. The term is also used for the post at the end of a stair handrail.

163 You can see the aurora borealis in the night sky of the Northern Hemisphere. It is a luminous display of flickering lights usually in the form of streams of coloured light. It is caused by streams of electrically charged particles from the sun, which are diverted towards the earth's magnetic poles. The particles collide with gases in the earth's atmosphere and change their electric charge. Aurorae have been shown to be linked with

sunspot activity and magnetic storms on earth. The aurora
borealis is also known as the 'Northern lights'. In the
Southern Hemisphere a similar phenomenon is known as
aurora australis or 'Southern lights'.

164 The Great Geyser is in south-western Iceland, and is a
hot spring that sends up a jet of hot water from the
ground. It is caused by underground water meeting
extremely hot rocks. The water cannot boil because of the
weight of the water above it. Steam begins to form, and
some water is pushed out, lightening the burden, until
there is suddenly an explosion of hot water and steam.
There are many such geysers in Iceland, and also in New
Zealand and the United States.

Sports and games 1

165 A game that has been won 'to love', i.e. without the loss
of a point.

166 A let is usually a serve that touches the net and lands
fair. 'Let' balls do not count and the server must serve
again. An umpire can call a 'let' whenever something
untoward happens that would necessitate the point
being played again, as when the ball is served before the
receiver is ready.

167 A batsman who is sent in to play out the last few overs
or balls of the day rather than risk the wicket of a better
batsman.

168 Players carry out a scissors movement by crossing before
completing a pass.

169 The shuttlecock is used in badminton, which used to be
called battledore and shuttlecock. Shuttlecocks, known
commonly as *shuttles*, have a round cork base (diameter
1 to 1⅛ inch) covered with leather and weighted with lead

shot. Set in the cork are 14 to 16 goose feathers from $2\frac{1}{2}$ to $2\frac{3}{4}$ inches long. Plastic shuttlecocks are now permitted. They last longer than feather ones, but do not reproduce the same flight in the air.

170 The team plays as 4 forwards, 2 link men and 4 defenders (plus the goalkeeper).

171 In the tug-of-war.

172 The slow bicycle race.

173 A bully-off is the preliminary crossing of sticks at the start or restart of a hockey game.

174 A scrum, or scrummage, is a tight mass of forward players from both teams in rugby football, who, locked together, try to get possession of the ball thrown into the middle.

175 Bowls. Other sporting 'greens' including the putting green in golf and the village green on which cricket may be played.

176 Golf is played on links, which is a term for a stretch of gently undulating land usually along a sea shore.

177 The telescopic fork holds the front wheel. It consists of double tubes, one moving inside the other like the action of a telescope. When the front wheel meets uneven ground, the fork telescopes so that the motor-cycle rides the bump without the rider feeling any discomfort. The whole movement is damped by means of oil.

178 A spinnaker is used in sailing. It is a full sail, used to catch the wind. It is carried on the mainmast of a racing yacht or dinghy running before the wind to give more speed.

179 He is called the *stroke*.

180 The hop, step and jump.

181 You kick up one leg so that the ski is standing upright, then lower the ski, turning it outwards and downwards. so that it faces in the reverse direction (backwards). You lift the other ski round and place it parallel to the first ski, and are then facing in the opposite direction.

The operation must be performed quickly, and balance depends on skilful use of the sticks.

182 You let the ball fall from your hands to the ground and kick it on the half-volley, i.e. just as it bounces.

183 Badminton.

184 A player is dummy when his partner is declarer (plays the hand). The player who first named the suit that won the contract is the declarer. Dummy places his hand (the dummy hand) face up on the table after the opponent to his right has played the first card. Declarer plays both his own hand and the dummy.

The world of nature

185 In a pouch.

186 On its back. Until it is about six months old, the young cub is carried in the pouch.

187 Live out of water as well as in it. Strictly speaking, amphibians lay their eggs in water and as adults live on land, but the name is given to creatures which can live in and out of water.

188 A backbone or spinal column.

189 He sleeps all day in summer and hibernates during the winter.

190 Hares are especially active in this month. They jump up and down, twist their bodies in the air, and act as though they were drunk. Two hares together will sometimes spar as if they were boxing.

191 A flower (common arum or wake-robin).

192 A froth given out by the larvae of certain insects. It is used for protection.

193 A gnawing animal such as a rat. It has strong incisor and no canine teeth.

194 An animal that carries its young in a pouch, such as a kangaroo.

195 A mammal is an animal that suckles its young.

196 The bat.

197 Unlike all other mammals (except spiny anteaters), the platypus lays eggs instead of bearing its young alive.

198 Every four or five years vast numbers of these lemmings begin to spread out in all directions. The urge to travel becomes so strong that they stop for nothing. They even tumble over cliffs and swim on until they drown. They are small rodents, about the size of rats, and live in cold regions, including Canada and Greenland as well as Scandinavia (mainly Norway).

199 The brown. Both its eyes are on this side. Secondly, this side is the camouflage side, the brown colouring matching the sea-bed. Halibut, a flat fish, habitually lies on its side at the bottom of the sea, and consequently only the upper, exposed side is coloured, the hidden underside remaining white.

200 The giraffe lives in Africa (mostly dry, almost desert, regions). It enjoys some leaves that only grow high up on trees. With its long neck, it can reach them while other animals cannot. It eats especially mimosa and acacia leaves.

201 He introduced a scientific method of naming plants and animals by putting them into groups or families. Karl von Linne (renamed Carolus Linnaeus), 1707–1778, was a Swede. In his system, every living thing had a name with two parts: first the genus or group; second the species or kind.

202 He studied and discovered the principles of heredity. He grew successive generations of plants and studied how certain characteristics were inherited. Gregor Johann Mendel (1822–1884) was an Austrian botanist and monk.

203 It is excellently camouflaged for its home in reeds. It has dark streaks in its plumage which therefore resembles reeds. When disturbed, it stands still and stretches its slender body and long neck upwards, again resembling reeds.

204 It originally came from eastern Asia, mainly China. Moreover, it is one of the most colourfully plumaged birds in the world, and therefore takes after the mandarins who wore beautifully ornamented robes of office.

General knowledge 4

205 Robin Hood.

206 King Arthur.

207 Anthracite is a very hard coal that burns slowly with great heat and little smoke.

208 A Bedouin is a nomad Arab. Bedouins roam the deserts of Arabia, Syria and northern Africa. They are tent dwellers and tend herds of sheep, camels and horses. Most Bedouins are Arabs.

209 A tandem is a two-seater.

210 On the back of a motor-cycle or scooter on the seat behind the driver. Or you might be on a horse behind the rider. The term *pillion* comes from the name of the cushion used by a woman riding behind a horseman. It was attached to the back of an ordinary saddle.

211 Kuwait is wealthy because of the income derived from its vast oil resources. The huge oil reserves were discovered in 1934. The government of Kuwait granted concessions to foreign oil companies for the extraction of oil in return for royalties.

212 The Rhine flows through the heart of Europe. Its waters are deep and calm enough and the river is wide enough to take large river boats and barges. Consequently it is

used by a number of countries (especially France, Germany and the Netherlands) to carry goods either from town to town or to the sea.

213 Brown. Demerara is a course, light brown, raw sugar.

214 Platinum is a silvery white. It is like silver but not as bright. When reduced to a powder, platinum can be black.

215 In feudal times the ringing of the curfew bell was a signal to put out all lights and fires and to stay indoors. In recent years, curfews have been imposed to prevent nocturnal conspiracies in various countries where there have been national disturbances. In these cases the curfew is a restriction to keep people indoors after a certain time. In the United States some localities have a curfew hour after which children are not allowed on the streets unaccompanied by adults.

216 Reveille sounds in the morning, often about sunrise. It is a military waking signal sounded on the bugle or drums.

217 The Board's symbol is a lion. They also stamp each egg with a number and a grading – large, medium or small – depending on the weight of the egg.

218 A torch, or two children with satchels, or two running children.

219 They both wrote diaries, Pepys from 1660 to 1669 and Evelyn from 1640 to 1706. They both also showed the spirit of scientific inquiry and were both Fellows of the Royal Society.

220 The woman was flung into a pool and if she did not drown she was 'proved' to be a witch. This meant that she died either way – by drowning or by being put to death for being a witch.

221 Mary Arden was Shakespeare's mother.

222 Sir Basil Spence was the architect, and Graham Sutherland designed the tapestry.

223 Rowland Hill wrote the pamphlet. It led to the reform of the Post Office in Britain, which brought in many

principles now accepted all over the world. These include payment by postage stamp, a common cheap rate, book post and packet post.

224 Charles Darwin wrote the treatise, the first scientific statement of the theory of evolution, which is now fairly commonly accepted. Darwin maintained that in nature there is a constant struggle for survival, and that those best fitted for the struggle survive.

Far-away places

225 Chinese junk.

226 In Africa, between Rhodesia and Zambia.

227 David Livingstone was the explorer. He named the falls after Queen Victoria.

228 The Himalayas.

229 The Alps.

230 The Sargasso Sea is in the North Atlantic Ocean, between the West Indies and the Azores. It contains large masses of floating seaweed in which many creatures live.

231 The Dogger Bank is in the North Sea, between England and Denmark. It consists mainly of sand, and is covered by water only about 50 to 100 feet deep.

232 The Pennines.

233 The Cotswolds.

234 Fujiyama (sometimes known as Fujisan). It is a volcano, now believed extinct, situated south-west of Tokyo. It is a centre for Buddhist pilgrimages.

235 Table Mountain.

236 Tanzania (formerly Tanganyika). Kilimanjaro is a volcano believed to be extinct.

237 Mexico – another volcano believed extinct.

238 In the industrial Midlands of England, around Birmingham. Other important towns include

Wolverhampton and Walsall.

239 The Wash is a wide bay of the North Sea between Lincolnshire and Norfolk, in East Anglia. It is an extension of the Fenland.

240 Djakarta.

241 Kuala Lumpur.

242 From the Rocky Mountains, in western North America. The chinook is a warm dry wind which descends the eastern slopes of the Rockies. It is also the name of a warm wind of the Oregon and Washington coasts, first named because it came from the direction of the Chinook Indian territory.

Speed quiz 3 – animals

243 A vixen.

244 A buck.

245 A mammal.

246 A mammal.

247 The Arctic.

248 The Antarctic.

249 Antlers (most stag deer and the female reindeer).

250 Tusks.

251 Birds. An aviary is a large cage for keeping birds in captivity.

252 Eagles.

253 Australian koala.

254 Buffalo. This is not the correct name, because the bison belongs to a different genus from that of the true buffalo.

255 North America – it is a prairie wolf.

256 Australia.

257 The squirrel. Dreys are built in trees of sticks and moss.

258 The beaver or otter.

259 A set or an earth.

260 A form. This is hardly a 'home' – it is just a place in
the open where the hare lies crouched and concealed
for most of the day and night.

261 Bees.

262 Ants.

General knowledge 5

263 The pyramids were the tombs of the Egyptian kings.
They had to be big and strong because the kings were
regarded as gods, and therefore their tombs had to remain
for ever. The tombs were filled with splendid things
because it was thought that the king would need all his
wealth and possessions in the other world to which his
spirit had already passed.

264 The Colosseum is an ancient amphitheatre in Rome.
Cruel spectacles took place there, frequently with
unwilling performers. Gladiators fought with each other or
with wild beasts. Christians were persecuted and killed
in the Colosseum.

265 Pussy willows are catkins that grow on the willow trees.
They are thought to be like tiny kittens climbing up the
twig, because they are soft and furry like kittens' tails.
(Catkins are the flowers of some trees.)

266 The Lady's Smock is a wild flower found on wet or
marshy ground.

267 There is no interest on Premium Bonds, but lottery
prizes from £25 to £25,000 are given. There is no lottery
with National Savings Certificates. The interest accrues
annually in the form of an addition to the value of each
certificate.

268 A person can go to the bank that issued an uncrossed
cheque and draw the actual cash amount. But with a

crossed cheque he can only put it through his own bank account, the value of the cheque being paid into it. Crossed cheques are safer, because if they fall into the wrong hands they must be passed through an account, which can afterwards be easily traced.

269 Copper (95%), tin (4%) and zinc (1%).

270 Silver coins are made of cupro-nickel, i.e. copper (75%) and nickel (25%).

271 A waterspout is a column of water between sea and cloud. Waterspouts occur in the tropics. An inverted cone of cloud descends from a heavy cumulo-nimbus cloud till it meets a cone of spray raised from the sea. The two join to form a column several hundred feet high. Strong winds circulate around it. Finally it breaks up and disappears. A waterspout might be described as a tornado occurring at sea.

272 A dust devil is a local whirl of dust sweeping round and round in a tall column, and moving slowly over the desert. It is not actually caused by the wind but is a phenomenon of convection caused by the heating of the desert.

273 The duke's house was called Blenheim in honour of his great victory over the French at Blenheim, near Augsburg in Bavaria. The battle took place on 13 August 1704 between France and Bavaria on the one side and England and Austria on the other. The royal manor of Woodstock was granted to the duke within a few months of his victory, and the mansion begun in 1705.

274 The name 'Holland', a fertile fen and marshland area in Lincolnshire, means 'land overlooked by high ground'. It is not named after Holland, the common name for the Netherlands. Holland in Lincolnshire was mentioned in the Doomsday Book, before the Dutch 'Holland' existed.

275 Information about earthquakes.

276 The height of the plane above sea level. This is measured by means of the decrease in atmospheric pressure with

height. A radio altimeter measures the plane's height
above ground by means of reflected radio waves.

277 A battle between the police and two alleged anarchists in
a house in Sidney Street, London. It took place in 1911
when Winston Churchill was Home Secretary. He
watched the operations in top hat and overcoat.

278 A whistle-stop tour is a high-powered electioneering tour
in which the candidate (often for president) visits a large
number of places to speak. It is so called because at one
time such tours were conducted from trains, and the
whistle went at various stages to attract audiences.

279 Showboats were floating theatres. The boats travelled
along rivers, particularly the Ohio and the Mississippi,
and actors aboard gave stage performances at places on
the route.

280 A 'son et lumière' (sound and light) is an evening pageant
using floodlights and sound amplifiers, usually centred
upon buildings with historic significance. Voices and
music are recorded and reproduced stereophonically
while changes in mood and colour of the lighting reflect
and heighten the dramatic points of the sound track.

281 A paradox is a figure of speech or a statement which at
first sight appears to be contradictory, but which is often
revealed on closer examination as having much wisdom
in a particular context.

282 A mixed metaphor is a statement in which one or more
metaphors are misused with a confusing, and often
humorous, result. For example, 'I smell a rat; I see it in
the air; but I will nip it in the bud.'

People of long ago 1

283 Hannibal was the general. He attacked the Romans
in Italy. To do this he took his war elephants across the

south of France and over the Alps, where he lost most of them.

284 Alexander the Great was the conqueror. Bucephalus was given to Alexander when he was only a boy. He tamed it, and no one else dared to touch or ride it. Bucephalus died in India, and Alexander built the city of Bucephala in its memory.

285 James, who became James VI of Scotland (1567) and James I of England (1603).

286 Oliver Cromwell (his son Richard succeeded him as Lord Protector in 1658 until the Restoration in 1660). Other leaders were known as 'The Protector' when acting as regent during the minorities of various kings.

287 He was supposed to have stood outside castles singing a verse of a song they had composed. He established contact when Richard's voice from inside the castle replied with the next verse. During the Third Crusade, Richard was imprisoned in the Castle of Duerenstein, on the Danube.

288 Nell Gwyn sold oranges. She later became an actress.

289 Julius Caesar was the general (Full name, Caius Julius Caesar). Caesar led the attack on Britain. At a moment of hesitation, the standard-bearer of the Tenth Legion leapt from one of the Roman warships and urged his men to follow him. This action turned the battle in the Romans' favour and made the first invasion of Britain successful.

290 Edward, The Black Prince, son of Edward III, commanded one of the divisions at the Battle of Crécy (1346) when he was only 16. He showed great courage in facing the well-armed French who outnumbered the English. He was hard pressed at one point and his fellow commander appealed to the king, who had command of the reserve, for reinforcements. The king refused to send help, saying: 'Let the boy win his spurs.' The English won, and the Black Prince had won his spurs.

291 Llewellen (ap Griffith Griffydd), who in return recognized
     Henry as his overlord (1267). This was the first official
     use of the title 'Prince of Wales'.

292 King Edward I, because he hammered at the Scots to try
     to get submission.

293 Richard Arkwright invented the water frame for cotton
     spinning. This was a water-powered spinning machine
     that superseded the hand-carding of cotton.

294 The abolition of slavery in Britain. Wilberforce was a
     great reformer and also supported educational reform,
     Catholic emancipation and missionary societies.

295 Agamemnon.

296 Penelope.

297 He was known as 'Chinese Gordon' because he suppressed
     the Taiping rebels in China in 1863–64. He is better
     known for the siege of Khartoum, which he defended for
     317 days. He was killed two days before help came.

298 David Lloyd George, who earned the title for his power
     of oratory. He became Minister of Munitions and then
     Prime Minister.

Team quiz 3

299a Eros is in Piccadilly Circus. It is of aluminium and was
      erected in 1885 as a memorial to the seventh Earl of
      Shaftesbury. The sculptor, Sir Alfred Gilbert, intended the
      boy with the bow to represent the Angel of Christian
      Charity, but the statue is usually referred to as Eros
      (the Greek god of love).

299b Nelson's column is in Trafalgar Square. Nelson died in
      1805 and the memorial was erected in 1842. The column
      was designed by W. Railton and the statue of Nelson,
      on top, by E. H. Bailey. The four lions at the foot of the
      column were added in 1867, all cast from an original
      modelled by Landseer.

300a The Cenotaph commemorates the 'Glorious Dead' of the world wars. The word (which comes from the Greek) means *empty tomb*. It is a burial monument to a person whose body is elsewhere. The Cenotaph, which is in Whitehall, was designed by Sir Edwin Lutyens, and unveiled in 1920 on Armistice Day by King George V.

300b The Monument commemorates the Great Fire of London (1666). It is supposed to be built 202 feet from the place in Pudding Lane where the fire began. Sir Christopher Wren built it between 1671 and 1677. It has a spiral stone staircase inside with over 300 steps.

301a Cleopatra's needle stands on the Thames Embankment near Charing Cross. It is an obelisk from ancient Egypt. About 70 feet high, it was given by an Egyptian ruler to Britain in the 1800s. It was one of a pair from Heliopolis, dating from about 1500 B.C. The other one was given to America and is now in New York's Central Park.

301b Speaker's Corner is at the Marble Arch end of Hyde Park. It is an open space where people gather to hear speakers on a vast variety of topics – religious, political, social, etc. Anyone who wants to make a speech can climb on to a box and do so.

302a To the Public Record Office in Chancery Lane, near Temple Bar. The Domesday Book is the record of William the Conqueror's survey of England in the eleventh century.

302b To Apsley House in Piccadilly, near Hyde Park Corner. It is the former home of the duke and was opened as the Wellington Museum in 1952.

303a A drawbridge is a bridge hinged at one end and free at the other so that it can be drawn up in order to prevent anyone crossing or to open the channel for passage underneath the bridge.

303b A swing bridge is a bridge that can be swung aside, swivelling on a pier in the middle, as a whole or in sections to allow a ship to pass.

304a An aqueduct is an artificial channel, like a bridge, which carries water. It can also be a small canal in the head of mammals. Bridges over valleys are commonly called aqueducts.

304b A pontoon bridge is one built on boats or floating piers, usually as a temporary measure by soldiers or scouts.

305a A suspension bridge is one held up by means of chains or cables which hang between high towers. The chains or cables pass over the tops of the towers and are securely anchored in the ground. Cables can be more than 3 feet thick and are made of thousands of high-strength steel wires.

305b A bascule bridge is a kind of drawbridge that is drawn up either in the middle or at one end to allow ships to pass.

306a The Rialto Bridge in Venice. The Rialto, a market at one end of the bridge, is mentioned several times in *The Merchant of Venice*.

306b It is in Venice, and is called the Bridge of Sighs because prisoners crossed it on their way to being punished or tried.

307a Spain.

307b Italy.

308a Money that has been forged, or illegally made.

308b Blood money is money paid to an informer who surrenders a criminal or gives information so that he can be caught.

309a He deals with the bank's customers, taking and paying out money at the counter. (A meaning of *tell* is to *count*).

309b A usurer lends money at an exorbitant rate of interest.

310a The sterling area refers to those countries that use the pound as the official exchange currency.

310b Specie is coin as opposed to paper currency.

General knowledge 6

311 A gate-crasher is a person who gets into a party or meeting although not invited.

312 A bulldozer is a machine used for levelling and clearing ground. The term may also be applied to a person who bullies or crashes his way through anything.

313 A tor is a hill or rocky peak.

314 Mountain.

315 South Africa has the biggest gold mine in the world. It is in the Transvaal.

316 At Fort Knox, in Kentucky.

317 Wine or spirit. A decanter is the stoppered glass vessel into which wines or spirits are 'decanted', i.e. poured off so that the sediment is left behind.

318 Water. A hydrant is a pipe (especially in the street) with a nozzle to which a hose can be attached for drawing water direct from the main.

319 Chileans speak Spanish, the official language.

320 Brazilians speak Portuguese, the official language.

321 A *meteor*, or 'shooting star', is a lump of matter from outer space which is rendered luminous by contact with the earth's atmosphere. If it does not completely burn up as it travels through the atmosphere, it falls to the ground as a *meteorite*.

322 *Icebergs* are masses of floating ice that have broken off glaciers; *ice-floes* have become detached from the main mass of polar ice.

323 Stamp duty is a duty on documents having a legal operation, usually concerned with property.

324 An arabesque is a position in which the dancer stands on one leg, bends forward from the hips, and extends the other leg backwards.

325 Ships have stabilizers to reduce rolling. Stabilizers are horizontal underwater fins attached to each side of the hull. Machinery inside the ship moves the fins up and down automatically to act against the waves and reduce the ship's roll.

326 A cathedral has the bishop's throne. A church has not.

327 A baronet's title is hereditary; a knight's is not.

328 *a* Norman *b* Early English *c* Decorated *d* Perpendicular Gothic.

Speed quiz 4

329 Mars.

330 Neptune.

331 Jupiter (or Zeus in Greek Mythology).

332 Juno (or Hera in Greek mythology). She was the goddess of marriage.

333 Mercury (or Hermes in Greek mythology).

334 Diana.

335 Bacchus.

336 Minerva (or Athena in Greek mythology).

337 (i) Japan   (ii) United States
    (iii) U.S.S.R. (Russia)   (iv) China (Communist)
    (v) Egypt (U.A.R.)   (vi) India
    (vii) Cuba   (viii) Indonesia.

338 A wizard or warlock.

339 A squaw.

340 A sultana.

341 A marchioness.

342 A stallion.

343 A vixen.

344 Gertrude.

The Bard of Avon

345 In *Julius Caesar*, they assassinate Caesar.

346 In *Macbeth*, Macbeth kills King Duncan.

347 Pretending that nothing is good enough for Katharina, his wife, Petruchio acts like an ill-tempered oaf, refusing to let her have any comfort or even food. He bullies her until he tames her obstinancy.

348 Portia says that Shylock can have the pound of flesh to which he is entitled, but if he spills one drop of blood or takes a fraction more than a pound of flesh, his property will be confiscated and his life forfeited.

349 Silver (the casket that the Prince of Arragon chooses).

350 The lead casket, with the inscription 'Who chooseth me must give and hazard all he hath'.

351 He snubs him ('I know thee not, old man') and banishes him ('not to come near our person by ten mile') on pain of death.

352 He refuses him the Earldom of Hereford which had been promised to him, and ultimately has him beheaded.

353 *Twelfth Night*. The words are spoken by Orsino, Duke of Illyria.

354 Puck, in *A Midsummer Night's Dream*.

355 In *Hamlet*, the ghost of Hamlet's father appears.

356 In *Macbeth*, Lady Macbeth walks in her sleep.

357 Malvolio is Olivia's pompous steward in *Twelfth Night*.

358 Caliban is the misshapen monster who is Prospero's slave in *The Tempest*.

359 Goneril, Regan and Cordelia.

360 The witches prophesied that Macbeth would become (1) Thane of Glamis, (2) Thane of Cawdor and (3) King.

361 The troops attacking Macbeth camouflage themselves with branches from the trees of Birnam.

362 There were six yokels altogether: (Peter) Quince, (Francis) Flute, (Tom) Snout, (Nick) Bottom, (Robin) Starveling and Snug.

363 He wore yellow stockings (and was cross-gartered).
Sir Toby Belch and his cronies had tricked Malvolio
into believing that this was what Olivia wished, although
he was in fact quite wrong.

364 The play is *Julius Caesar*. Caesar's wife, Calpurnia, has
dreamed of his death.

365 *Romeo and Juliet*.

366 *Antony and Cleopatra*.

Team quiz 4 – far-away places

367a Rhine.

367b Seine.

368a St. Lawrence.

368b Danube.

369a Rhône.

369b Nile.

370a Congo.

370b Ganges.

371a The Broads lie near the east coast of England, in Norfolk
and northern Suffolk. They make up a region of flat land
with shallow lakes, marshes and slow-moving rivers.

371b The Downs lie in southern England, extending eastwards
from mid-Hampshire across Surrey. They consist of
regions of hills, called the North Downs and the South
Downs. The region has rolling hills and good farm and
pasture land in the district known as the Weald.

372a The Pampas are in South America. They are vast,
grass-covered plains, making good pasture land for sheep
and cattle. The term is most commonly used for the plain
in central Argentina and Uruguay.

372b The Rockies, or Rocky Mountains, are a chain of
mountains in the western part of North America. They
extend for more than 3,000 miles from northern New

Mexico to northern Alaska, and consist mainly of jagged snow-capped peaks. A few have gentle slopes and rounded tops. The Rockies are famous for their scenic beauty, and many national parks are located in the region.

373a The most well-known fjords are in Norway. They are long, narrow inlets of the sea. Most fjords have steep, rocky walls with thick woods and foaming, roaring waterfalls. Small stretches of fertile farm land lie below some of the cliffs. The coasts of Alaska and Maine, in the United States, and British Columbia and New Zealand also have fjords.

373b The Himalayas are a range of mountains lying north of India and south of China. They separate northern India from the plateau of Tibet. They consist of snowy mountain peaks, and are very black and desolate. 'Himalaya' means 'snowy range of house of snow'. Some of the highest mountains in the world are in the Himalayas, including Mount Everest, the highest (29,000 feet).

374a The Polders are in the Netherlands. They are areas of flat land reclaimed from the sea and protected by dikes and dams.

374b The Tundra lie round the Arctic Ocean. They are low swampy plains with a few scattered shrubs but no full-sized trees. What vegetation there is consists mainly of mosses, lichens, and dwarf trees. The Tundra region is perpetually frozen to a great depth, except for a few feet at the surface which thaws in the brief Arctic summer. The frozen ground is known as *permafrost*. Parts of northern Europe, Siberia and North America are in the Tundra region.

375a Nippon. It means 'the land of the rising sun'.

375b Fujiyama. Its name in English is Mount Fuji. *Yama* means *mountain*.

376a Kimono.

376b   Geisha girls.

377a   To feed the silkworms that spin silk.

377b   Rice.

378a   A vehicle pulled or pedalled by a man. The word means
'man-powered cart'.

378b   Ju-jitsu is a form of self-defence similar to wrestling.
Contestants score points by three methods: (1) by
throwing their opponent to the ground, (2) by applying
a choking or strangling hold, or a limb lock, and
exerting pressure until their opponent submits, or (3) by
forcing their opponent's back to the ground for thirty
seconds.

The world of science

379   Contraction following upon a sudden change in temperature causes the glass to break.

380   It is a gas burner for heating substances and is used
mainly in scientific laboratories. Two openings at the
bottom of the tube control the amount of air that mixes
with the gas, which makes it possible for it to give great
heat. Air mixing with gas before burning produces a
flame without smoke.

381   It turns blue. And blue litmus turns red in an acid solution.

382   Aluminium foil has a shiny surface that reflects the heat.
It does not let much heat pass out by radiation. The
heat from the central heating installation is therefore
kept largely within the confines of the house, and only
leaks out very slowly.

383   Because rubber is a good insulation against electricity,
and therefore protects electricians against electric shocks.

384   Because it will not burn and is remarkable for its
resistance to heat. Although asbestos is a mineral, it
can be spun into cloth. It disintegrates at extremely high

temperatures. It resists acids, alkalines and other
chemicals.

385 Galileo Galilei was the scientist. The story, which is
disputed, has it that Galileo dropped two weights (1 lb
and 10 lb) from the Leaning Tower of Pisa to prove
his Theory that gravity pulls all bodies to earth with the
same acceleration regardless of their weight. Both weights
struck the ground at the same time, and Galileo had
proved his point.

386 Einstein's famous equation (Energy equals mass times the
velocity of light squared) is the foundation stone in the
development of atomic energy.

387 Each lens has two parts – the upper part is used for
distant vision, the lower part for close vision.

388 A contact lens is a small plastic lens worn directly on the
eyeball, floating in the layer of tears covering the cornea
and front surface of the eye, and in a position opposite the
pupil. Contact lenses cannot be seen. They are wetted by
the eye blinking, and are thus prevented from steaming
up or getting spotted by rain.

389 The gas can be stored as a liquid in metal containers.
In this form it is usually concentrated, safe and easily
portable. When the valve on a container is opened, the
fuel escapes as a gas and can be used in this form.

390 Mercury freezes (and therefore does not register) when
the temperature falls below –38°C. Alcohol has a much
lower freezing point, − 114·5°C.

391 The fan or pump makes a vacuum (or partial vacuum)
within the cleaner. Outside air tries to fill the vacuum and
dirt and dust is taken in with it. Some vacuum cleaners
remove the dirt by suction only. Others have a stiff
brush or a set of agitator bars that loosens the dust in the
carpet and helps it into the container.

392 The inner bottle is made of glass, which is a poor
conductor of heat. The vacuum (or near vacuum) between

the two bottles slows down the convection of heat. The facing surfaces of the bottles are coated with a silvery solution which reduces radiation. The heat could be transferred through the stopper, and therefore it is made of cork or plastic, poor conductors of heat.

393   *Fission* means *splitting* heavy atoms into lighter atoms. *Fusion* means *uniting* lightweight atoms to get heavier atoms.

394   The *diode* has two electrodes: anode and cathode. The *triode* has an anode, a cathode and a control grid. The diode is used chiefly for rectification and demodulation.

395   The scientist was Louis Pasteur, a bacteriologist-chemist. The dog suffered from rabies, a killing disease if transferred from mad dog to human being. The little boy, Joseph Meister, was taken to Pasteur who cured him by inoculation – about 13 inoculations were given in the first ten days. Up till then there had been no cure.

396   The husband and wife team, Pierre and Marie Curie, obtained radium from the pitchblende.

General knowledge 7

397   A chorister is a person who sings in a choir, especially a boy in a church choir.

398   A page-boy is a boy who takes messages or runs errands, especially in a hotel or club. People of rank sometimes have personal attendants called page-boys, and some brides have a little boy to hold their train – also called a page-boy.

399   366 days.

400   Every four years there is a leap year. If the last two figures of a year are exactly divisible by 4, it is a leap year such as 1968. The only exceptions to the four-year rule are the last years in a century. Only when the year is

exactly divisible by four hundred is such a year a leap
year. For example, 1800 and 1900 were not leap years.
But the year 2000 will be. Leap years have an extra day
(February 29) and the reason for having them is to adjust
the calendar so that the days and seasons are consistent.
Otherwise they would get out of phase over the years
because there not an exact number of days (the time it
takes for the earth to spin round once on its axis) in a
year (the time it takes the earth to make a complete
revolution around the sun).

401 One who manages or directs the performances in the ring
of a circus.

402 A toast master is the man who announces guests, and
proposes toasts at a dinner or a public ceremony. A
toast is a drink in honour of someone. A toast master
is not a member of the party but is hired for the occasion.

403 We mean that the person is insincere. He pretends to be
virtuous but should not be trusted.

404 He does not allow his feelings to show in his expression.
The term is derived from poker, a card game in which
bluff plays a major part, and an expressionless, inscrutable
face prevents a player's opponents from guessing the
value of the cards he is holding.

405 France's basic monetary unit is the *franc*. There are
100 centimes in a franc.

406 The *mark*, or *Deutsch mark* (D.M.). There are 100
pfennigs in a D.M.

407 Salty – it is the chemical name of salt.

408 At the Vatican in Rome. They are the Papal Swiss Guard
and their uniform was designed by Michelangelo.

409 Scientists, called *palaeontologists*, learn about ancient
animals from *fossils*. Fossils are shells, bones, and other
traces of animals and plants buried in rocks. From a
study of fossils of prehistoric animals, scientists can tell
where the animals lived and what they were like.

410 Suspension is the connection, often by means of springs, between the wheels and the frame. With independent suspension, each wheel is completely independent of the others and no connecting axle beams are used. Each wheel gives according to the road surface but the car remains steady.

411 The night safe is situated in the outside wall of a bank. It has a metal sliding door which can be opened by customers who are provided with a key. Money to be deposited is locked in a wallet and placed on a shelf inside the door of the safe, and when the door is closed the wallet is tipped down into the bank's strong room. Night safes make it possible, among other things, for shopkeepers to deposit their day's takings at a bank after it is closed.

412 Some banks allocate space in their strong rooms in which customers can store their valuables, such as documents, jewellery, etc. The customer has a locker and a key which he can use to inspect or add to or take away from his possessions in the safe deposit locker.

413 A customs' union is a group of countries who have agreed a common external tariff. Benelux is a customs' union of Belgium, the Netherlands and Luxembourg. The Common Market aims to be a customs' union.

414 Traveller's cheques are notes that can be exchanged abroad for foreign currency. They have to be signed in the presence of the bank clerk who issues them, and countersigned, when used as a means of payment or when changed into foreign currency, in the presence of the person receiving them so that the two signatures can be compared. They are issued in denominations of £2, £5, £10, £20, and £50. They can be used at home as well as abroad, and would be acceptable where personal cheques might not be.

415 The United Nations Educational, Scientific, and Cultural

Organization. It was established to contribute to peace and security by promoting collaboration among the nations through education, science and culture in order to further universal respect for justice, law and human rights.

416 The European (Space Vehicle) Launcher Development Organization. Countries taking part are Australia (firing range facilities), Britain (first stage, Blue Streak), France (second stage), West Germany (third stage), Italy (satellite test vehicle), and the Netherlands (long-range telemetry). Denmark is an observer country. The initial programme was a European three-stage satellite.

Team quiz 5

417a Christopher Columbus.

417b The Pilgrim Fathers.

418a The *Queen Elizabeth* and the *Queen Mary*. They were superseded by the *Queen Elizabeth II*.

418b The *Golden Hind* and the *Pelican*. The ship was rechristened.

419a A clipper. It was one of the fastest sailing ships of the last century, and is on exhibition to the public at Greenwich, in London.

419b A submarine. It was the first nuclear-powered warship. A nautilus is a genus of deep-sea molluscs.

420a It was torpedoed by the Germans.

420b It struck an iceberg, in 1912.

421a A soldier. It is a tall fur cap worn by the Guards.

421b A sailor or a fisherman. It is a waterproof hat with a flap to cover the back of the neck.

422a Cowboys. They are broad-rimmed hats.

422b Scotsmen. They are circular, flat-topped caps.

423a A tall, red, brimless cap, like an upturned bucket, with

a coloured tassel. They were first made in the town of
Fez, in Morocco, but are usually associated with the
Turks. The wearing of the fez was banned in Turkey by
Kemal Ataturk in 1927, but some Turks still wear them.

423b A long scarf wound round and round the top of the head.
Indians and Pakistanis wear turbans.

424a Graduates, teachers, professors, and students might wear
a mortarboard. It is the 'cap' that goes with the 'gown'
that signifies scholastic success. The cap is round, with
a square, flat board on top with a tassel. The
mortarboard is so-called because it resembles the board
used by builders for carrying mortar.

424b A bishop. It is a tall cap with a cleft at the top.

425a A lumberjack fells trees. He also saws and removes trees,
especially in North America.

425b A dietician is an authority on diets and the calorific
value of food. He prepares diets for people.

426a A steeplejack is a man who works on high buildings or on
high metal-framed constructions.

426b A frogman works under water, usually on the hulls of
ships, clearing underwater obstructions. The term
originated in wartime, when frogmen used to clear mines
or attach explosives to ships.

427a A contortionist twists or distorts his body into extreme
positions and postures. The term can also be used of
one who twists words and phrases.

427b A statistician analyses figures. He collects and arranges
numerical facts and data, i.e. statistics.

428a An astronomer studies the stars and planets scientifically.
An astrologer claims to foretell the future by the aspect
and situations of the heavenly bodies.

428b An archaeologist studies the cultural remains and
monuments of the remote past. (His science is called
archaeology.) An anthropologist studies the nature of
man, including his physiological, social and religious

development. (His science is called anthropology.)

429a A poacher.

429b A veterinary surgeon. (vet.)

430a An architect.

430b An optician. (An oculist is an eye doctor.)

431a A coroner.

431b An ambassador. (Some Commonwealth representatives in London are called High Commissioners, as are many British representatives in Commonwealth countries.)

432a An anaesthetist.

432b A physiotherapist.

The Bible

433 Cain and Abel.

434 Leah and Rachel.

435 Herod (Matt. 2:13 – 'For Herod will seek the young child, to destroy him').

436 John the Baptist (Luke 1.)

437 Balthazar, Caspar and Melchior.

438 Gold, frankincense and myrrh.

439 He became angry when the Lord liked Abel's sacrifice of sheep better than his own sacrifice of grain ('Cain brought of the fruit of the ground an offering unto the Lord.' Gen. 4). He was jealous that Abel's sacrifice of the firstlings of his flock had been accepted by Jehovah, whereas his own was rejected.

440 In defiance of God's command, she turned round to look at the fiery destruction of the wicked cities of Sodom and Gomorrah. It was a punishment for her curiosity and disobedience. (Gen. 19)

441 Moses was the leader. God called him to the top of Mount Sinai and gave him two stone tablets on which were written the Ten Commandments.

442 On the way to arrest some Christians, he was struck blind
and heard Jesus calling to him. He was without sight for
three days and did not eat or drink. Ananias gave him
back his sight and converted him.

443 Goliath was the giant. David killed him by striking him
on the forehead with a stone from his sling. (I Sam. 17)

444 Samson was betrayed. Delilah cut off his hair, in which
his strength lay, or caused 'the seven locks of his head'
to be shaved, so that he was unable to resist capture by
the enemies she summoned.

445 The angel of the Lord spoke these words to the shepherds,
bringing them the news of the birth of Christ (Luke 2: 10).

446 Jesus spoke these words to His disciples after His
resurrection (Mark 16: 15).

447 They represented conquest, war, famine and death.
A scroll in God's right hand is sealed with seven seals
(Rev. 6.) When the first four of these seals are opened,
four horsemen appear. Their horses are white, red, black
and pale (possibly greenish-yellow).

448 (1) The Apostle's Doctrine, (2) Fellowship,
(3) Breaking of Bread and (4) Prayers (Acts 2: 42).

General knowledge 8

449 The scale shows how much of the actual earth's surface
is represented by a given measurement on a map.

450 Contour lines are lines drawn to join places at the same
height above sea level and depths below it.

451 A chiff-chaff is a bird of the warbler family, noted for
its song.

452 A cheetah is an animal of the cat family. Cheetahs come
from Africa and Asia. They stand about three to four
feet high and are also known as 'hunting leopards'.

453 The Sphinx and pyramids, Egypt.

454 They were fought by Christians to recapture the Holy Land, Palestine, where Jesus Christ had lived, and which was then occupied by Turks and Saracens.

455 A brush.

456 A pointer is a gun dog. When it locates its quarry it 'points', i.e. it stands quite still, staring in the direction of the quarry. It carries its head and neck outstretched. The higher its nose, the further it can smell, so it points to any bird in the area quicker. The retriever then retrieves the bird when it has been shot by the guns.

457 Trachea.

458 Larynx.

459 China.

460 On the eastern coast of the Mediterranean Sea, now the coastal areas of Syria, Lebanon and Israel.

461 In summer, anti-cyclones usually bring fine, calm, warm weather conditions. But in winter anti-cyclones often mean frosty nights, with fog developing particularly in smoke-polluted industrial areas.

462 Heavy continuous rain. The monsoon is a tropical seasonal wind in southern Asia. It blows approximately from the south-west in summer (wet and rainy) and from the north-east in winter (dry).

463 (1) Strasbourg   (2) Cologne   (3) Dusseldorf.

464 (1) Vienna   (2) Budapest   (3) Belgrade.

465 A limerick is a funny verse which has a definite pattern: five lines, with the first two lines and the last one rhyming, and with lines three and four rhyming.

466 An elegy is a song of lamentation, especially for the dead. A gravely thoughtful poem which is usually on the subject of someone's death. Examples are 'Lycidas' (Milton), 'Adonais' (Shelley) and 'In Memoriam' (Tennyson).

467 A crustacean, with few exceptions, is a shell-fish.

Crustaceans are a class of the *arthropods* (joint-footed animals) of which there are about ten thousand species. The most common crustaceans are the barnacle, crab, crayfish, lobster and shrimp. A woodlouse is also a crustacean.

468 Whales, porpoises and dolphins are cetaceans. They have torpedo-shaped bodies, fin-like forelimbs and no hind limbs. They live in fresh or salt water. They breathe with lungs and possess layers of oily fat called *blubber* (one inch thick in dolphins, one foot thick in whales).

Novels and poems

469 *Catriona* (also called *David Balfour*).
470 *Lorna Doone* (by R. D. Blackmore).
471 'Hohenlinden' by Thomas Campbell.
472 'The Lady of Shalott' by Alfred, Lord Tennyson.
473 Eighty days.
474 A scarlet pimpernel. In the stories, Blakeney helped the French Royalists to escape from France to England during the time of the Revolution at the end of the eighteenth century.
475 The daisy, in 'To a Mountain Daisy'.
476 Daffodils, in 'The Daffodils'.
477 C. S. Lewis, in *The Lion, the Witch and the Wardrobe*.
478 Dylan Thomas, in *Under Milk Wood*. This was his last work, which he completed for radio a month before his death, but was still revising for stage and book form.
479 'The Lady of the Lake' by Sir Walter Scott.
480 'Home Thoughts from Abroad', by Robert Browning.
481 She buried her brother Polyneices. In the play, called *Antigone*, King Creon forbade anyone to bury Polyneices because he had attacked his native city of Thebes. For Antigones' defiance, the king condemned her to be shut

up in a cave, where she hanged herself.

482 Triffids, in the science fiction novel by John Wyndham, *The Day of the Triffids*.

483 'To Autumn', by John Keats.

484 Jim was a lecturer in a provincial university.

Speed quiz 5 – far-away places

485 Stockholm.

486 Budapest.

487 Spain.

488 Denmark.

489 The North Sea.

490 The English Channel.

491 It is a town in New South Wales (Australia).

492 The Statue of Liberty in New York Harbour.

493 Somerset.

494 Italy.

495 Greece.

496 Greece.

497 Israel (near Jerusalem).

498 Turkey.

499 The eastern end of the Mediterranean coast of France. It is sometimes known as the French Riviera.

500 The northern end of the Mediterranean coast of Spain. It is the coastal strip of the province of Gerona, from the French frontier to Blanes.

501 Hook of Holland.

502 Dieppe.

503 Cambodia is north of the equator, in south-east Asia.

504 The Philippines are north of the equator, in the Pacific Ocean.

Sports and games 2

505 Swimming – they are both strokes.

506 Cricket. A *maiden* is an over in which no runs are scored
from the bat. A *wide* occurs when the bowler delivers the
ball so wide of the wicket or so high that, in the opinion
of the umpire, it is out of reach of the batsman.

507 A pyramid fence consists of three parts, with the highest
part in the middle. It is also called a 'hog's back'.

508 In tennis, the server has to put the ball in play for each
point by standing behind the baseline and hitting the ball
over the net into the serving area diagonally opposite
him. He gets two chances to do this, and if he misses
both, i.e. if he serves a *fault* on both, he has made a double
fault and loses that point. A player can serve a fault in
a number of ways, such as serving into the net or outside
the serving area, or fouling the base line with his foot or
lifting both feet off the ground. If a serve touches the top
of the net and falls in the service area, the ball does not
count and the player serves again (a 'let' is called).

509 Skin diving is swimming beneath the surface of the water
with the aid of varying types of apparatus, such as a
snorkel (a small pipe that enables the swimmer to breathe
air sucked from above the surface) or *aqualungs* (apparatus
containing compressed air in cylinders), and mask and
flippers to assist movement. Sometimes skin divers wear
a protective rubber suit in waters colder than 60°F.
Skin diving is usually treated as a sport; aqualung
swimming is sometimes referred to as 'free diving'.

510 Pat Moss Carlsson.

511 A set is won when one side wins at least six games and
the other side wins only four games or less. If each side
wins five games, then one side must win two consecutive
games to win the set.

512 A 4 is signalled by a horizontal sweep of the arm. A
6 is signalled by stretching the arms upwards in a V.

513   It is a horse race over a course defined by certain landmarks. It takes place in open country, with fences, and is sometimes organized by a hunt.

514   It is a motor-cycle race meeting in open country with natural hazards.

515   Thirteen.

516   Fifteen.

517   The All-Blacks are the New Zealand rugby team. It is so called because the team wears black jerseys.

518   The cyclist with the best aggregate time at the beginning of each stage is given the yellow jersey to wear to show that up to that time he is the potential winner.

519   The puck is a small rubber disc used in ice hockey. It glides over the ice.

520   A player must score two consecutive points.

521   Glasgow Celtic. They beat Inter Milan 2–1 at Lisbon in 1967.

522   It is the cup awarded to the country winning the men's world table tennis team championships.

523   Rod Laver of Australia. He beat Ken Rosewall, also of Australia, in the final in 1967.

524   Roger Bannister, who ran the mile in 3 minutes 59.4 seconds at Oxford on 6 May 1954.

Literature

525   Brobdingnag.

526   Biggles is an air pilot, who is prepared to carry out risky operations in any part of the world. The character was created by Captain W. E. Johns and is described in various ways, such as Air Detective, Inspector Bigglesworth, or Chief Operational Pilot.

527   Fagin is a character in Charles Dickens's *Oliver Twist*. He was a Jew and head of a gang of thieves including

Bill Sikes and the Artful Dodger. Fagin was a fence who received stolen property and trained boys to become pickpockets.

528 Ralph, Jack and Peterkin. *Coral Island* is by R. M. Ballantyne.

529 The story begins in the City of Destruction and ends in the Celestial City.

530 A pound of flesh.

531 £1.

532 Ebenezer Scrooge.

533 Mr (Wackford) Squeers.

534 The story is *Hansel and Gretel*. Gretel tricks the witch into peering into the oven. The witch is then given a shove and into the oven she goes. The oven falls apart and the gingerbread boys and girls come to life. The opera is by the German composer Engelbert Humperdinck.

535 The trolls hear the ringing of church bells in the valley. Henrik Ibsen, the Norwegian dramatist, wrote *Peer Gynt*.

536 Herman Melville wrote the novel *Moby Dick*, which was an enormous white whale.

537 Hugh Lofting, who illustrated his books himself.

538 Oscar Wilde in *The Importance of Being Earnest*.

Speed quiz 6

539 Tickets.

540 A spinney is a group of trees or a small wood.

541 A spy story.

542 A cowboy story or story of the Wild West.

543 Off the south-western coast of England, about thirty miles from Land's End.

544 Off the north coast of Scotland.

545 The *Mayflower*.

546   The *Santa María*. Other ships in the fleet were the
       Niña and the *Pinta*.

547   Euston.

548   Paddington.

549   In Monaco, a tiny principality on the French Riviera, but
       not a part of France.

550   The *Concorde*, a supersonic airliner being built jointly
       by Britain and France.

551   Your future.

552   The words for a musical work.

553   Tsar (also spelt Tzar, Czar).

554   A lorry that consists of two linked vehicles, one the
       truck and the other the engine and driver's cabin.

555   Cornwall.

556   London.

557   At the Tabard Inn, Southwark, in London.

558   The Cheshire Cheese. Their first meeting place was the
       King's Head, in Ivy Lane.

General knowledge 9

559   A spider. Miss Muffett was frightened away by a spider
       who sat down beside her. Robert the Bruce, when in the
       depths of despair about his native Scotland, was inspired
       by the persistent efforts of a spider to succeed in what he
       wanted to do.

560   An Apple. William Tell was supposed to have shot an
       apple from his son's head when challenged to do so.
       Isaac Newton said he thought of his theory about gravity
       when he saw an apple fall.

561   On the sea or a waterway. It is the French name for
       sea sickness.

562   Travelling on a railway train. It is the French name for
       railway.

563   The gravitational pull of the sun and the moon.

564 Salts are carried into the sea by the rivers.

565 It is a system of road crossings with sweeping curves which look like a huge clover leaf. Dry land bridges are used with ramps from one level to another so that traffic going in one direction crosses over or under traffic going in a cross-direction.

566 It is a device to show the direction of the wind. It is flown at an aerodrome, and looks like a sock open at both ends.

567 The eldest son of the King of France.

568 The eldest daughter of King and Queen of Spain or Portugal who is not heir to the throne.

569 *a* Fez *b* Beret *c* Bowler *d* Stetson.

570 A sky which has cirrus and cirrocumulus clouds, making a pattern of long, white clouds resembling the pattern on the back of a mackerel.

571 A marine insurer who agrees to assume part of the risk when a ship is insured.

572 A fitting on the bumper that stops the bumper getting damaged in a slight collision with another car.

573 Longarone is in northern Italy (Venetia). The dam above the village burst and drowned the village in the valley.

574 It is in Yugoslavia (the capital of the Yugoslav Republic of Macedonia). The tragedy was an earthquake disaster.

575 Prison reform. The league is named after John Howard who lived in the eighteenth century. Howard wrote a book exposing conditions in the prisons and spent a lot of time and a considerable fortune trying to improve them.

576 Clocks and watches.

Work this one out

577 1 acre.

578 2 inches per hour. (2.54 centimetres = 1 inch).

579 This is the time taken for the moon to make a complete orbit of the earth.

580 This is the measurement of the circumference of the earth at the equator.

581 It will take eleven seconds to strike 12 o'clock. The nine strokes at 9 o'clock are separated by eight equal intervals of time. The striking takes eight seconds altogether, so each interval must be one second long. There are eleven equal intervals separating the striking of 12. Therefore the time taken will be eleven seconds.

582 John got 69 and Bill 84. It is very easy to work this out if you appreciate that the total marks above the average should equal the total marks below. As Bill has 8 marks above and John 7 marks below, this means that David has 1 mark below (above and below both being 8). Therefore the average is $75 + 1 = 76$, and the marks of John and Bill are obtained by subtracting 7 and adding 8, respectively, to the average.

The problem may be tackled using algebra:

If x equals the class average,

$$\frac{(x - 7) + (x + 8) + 75}{3} = x$$

Therefore $2x + 76 = 3x$ and $x = 76$.

583 An acute angle.

584 A pentagon.

585 24 miles an hour. *Method:* Distance from destination is 4×30 miles $= 120$ miles. So at 20 miles an hour, the return journey takes 6 hours. This makes a total of 10 hours for a distance of 240 miles (twice 120). Therefore the average speed is $\frac{240}{10} = 24$ miles an hour.

586 £20 profit. There are two separate transactions with £10 profit on each one.

Team quiz 6

587a Guy Fawkes Day – the attempted blowing-up of Parliament in 1605.

587b All Fools' Day (commonly known as April Fools' Day).

588a The World War I armistice was declared.

588b VE Day. The Allies achieved Victory in Europe in World War II on 8 May 1945.

589a The longest day of the year – Summer Solstice (21 June). The Druids are members of a secret society who take their name from a supposed ancient order of priests.

589b Thanksgiving Day (remembering the Pilgrim Fathers).

590a The storming of the Bastille (a prison in Paris that was used for political prisoners). The day is a public holiday in France and is celebrated by Frenchmen everywhere.

590b The Declaration of Independence. Independence Day is a public holiday in the United States and is celebrated by Americans everywhere.

591a To obtain extra warmth. The mesh is supposed to retain an insulation of air. Wool vests also give this insulation, air being trapped in the wool mesh.

591b To prevent snow-blindness. The white surface of the snow reflects the sun and dazzles and harms the eyes. In extreme cases it can cause a temporary loss of sight.

592a Because in the event of an accident, spilt petrol is a serious fire hazard.

592b Water is a good conductor of electricity and lowers the body's resistance to current. If you touch an electrical device with wet hands, any fault in the device is more likely to cause electricity to pass through your body to earth.

593a To keep him under water without too much effort, and to help him to remain upright to do his work.

593b To enable him to control his movements in his cabin. Because of the weightlessness of matter in outer space, he might float around in his cabin without the help of the magnets.

594a Pickling prevents deterioration. The pickling fluid has properties of preservation, and permeates the perishable matter.

594b Oranges are a source of vitamin C, which is essential for healthy blood vessels and sound bones and teeth. People who lack this vitamin may have sore gums, haemorrhage under the skin and general fatigue.

595a The sides of the stage or pieces of side scenery are called the wings.

595b The flies are the part of a theatre above the stage where scenery can be hoisted and stored out of sight of the audience.

596a A property master is the person responsible for the 'props' or properties. He obtains all the articles needed on stage for a production and ensures that they are available when required. There is also a property master in a coal mine – he is in charge of equipment.

596b A stage manager is the person who supervises the physical aspects of a stage production, such as lighting, sets, technicians and stage staff. He assists the director during rehearsals, and is in complete charge of the stage during a performance.

597a An apron stage is an extension of the ordinary stage beyond what is known as the proscenium arch.

597b The denouement is the final unravelling of the plot or complications of a play.

598a Japan. *Kabuki* is a highly stylized form of drama, which developed from dancing. Stories and speeches are chanted by the performers.

598b Japan. The *no* play combines dancing, music and chanting – strung together in a simple plot. *No* developed from a religious dance, and is usually serious, with perhaps a tragic theme. A full performance of *no* (five plays in all) can last nearly a whole day.

599a   A republic is a state in which the government is carried on by the people or their selected representatives without a monarch.

599b   A group of states that form a unified body but remain independent in internal affairs, such as the United States.

600a   Constituents are the people who are entitled to vote and elect a member of parliament.

600b   A canvasser is a person who calls on the constituents to discuss the political issues at stake and put forward the claims of the candidate he is representing in order to solicit votes.

601a   The Cabinet is a group (usually of about twenty) of senior ministers that forms the policy-making body of the government. The prime minister chooses the Cabinet members.

601b   *Hansard* is the official, printed, verbatim report of pro-ceedings in Parliament.

602a   Sweden. The Riksdag consists of two chambers: Forsta Kammaren (151 members) and Andra Kammaren (233 members).

602b   Spain. The parliament of Portugal was also called the Cortes until 1911, when it was superseded by two elected chambers.

Speed quiz 7 – famous women

603   Helen of Troy.

604   Queen Victoria.

605   Queen Elizabeth I.

606   Catherine Parr. She outlived Henry.

607   Mary Rand.

608   Ann Packer.

609   Charlotte Brontë.

610 Jane Austen.
611 Lady Jane Grey in 1553.
612 Queen Mary I, who reigned from 1553 to 1558, married Philip II of Spain.

613 Cleopatra.
614 Dido.
615 Opera singing.
616 Ballet dancing.
617 Opera singing.

618 Poetry.
619 George Eliot.
620 George Sand.
621 Sculpture.
622 Music (composing).

General knowledge 10

623 Weddings. The place is noted for runaway marriages that used to be performed there.
624 A cricket match. Lords is the headquarters of English cricket and the ground of Middlesex and of the M.C.C.
625 Under water. A snorkel is a short breathing tube that may be fitted into a face mask worn by divers. The other end of the tube remains out of the water as the diver swims, thus allowing him to breathe while under water.
626 Usually in a hospital. It is an appliance to help a person to breathe, especially a polio patient.
627 On a railway engine's platform or carriage step.
628 On the staircase leading to a cabin on board a ship.
629 He was a highwayman, and many highwaymen were executed on the gallows at Tyburn (London), called Tyburn Tree.
630 It was not a normal tea party. The tea was tipped into the sea from the tea chests by Americans disguised as Indians, because they resented having to pay tax on tea to the British government.
631 Tacking is changing the course of a yacht by moving the sails to take full advantage of the wind. Course or movements of a ship are obliquely opposed to the

direction of the wind. A consecutive series of such movements to one side and the other alternately are made by a sailing vessel in order to reach a point windward.

632 He adjusts them with reference to the direction of the wind and the course of the ship so as to obtain full advantage of the available wind.

633 They project from the gutter of a building in order to carry rain water clear of the wall.

634 Stables. The word *mews* was originally used for the royal stables built on the site of the King's Mews for hawks where the birds were kept while 'mewing' or moulting.

635 Holy Orders are conferred for admission to the Ministry of the Church.

636 It is an installation into office. The term *investiture* is now used mainly to describe the ceremonies when the sovereign receives the newly appointed peers, knights and other new holders of titles and honours.

637 Robert Stephenson, with his father's help, constructed the London and Birmingham Railway which had its terminus in Euston.

638 They were railway engines, and *Rocket*, built by George Stephenson, won.

639 They were called Chindits. They were British Commandos who fought behind the Japanese lines in Burma in World War II cutting the lines of communications.

640 William Ewart Gladstone, the Liberal, was known as 'the People's Tribune'; Benjamin Disraeli, the Conservative, was called 'Dizzy'.

People of long ago 2

641 Boadicea.

642 Henry V.

643 James VI of Scotland and James I of England.

644 William Caxton, who set up his printing press in 1476 near Westminster Abbey. Caxton did not invent printing. He learnt the craft on the Continent.

645 He wore a crown of laurel, or bay leaves. He was drawn in a triumphal carriage by four horses along the Via Sacra at the head of a procession to the Capitol. Under the empire only the emperor could receive a triumph. A great general received an 'ovation'.

646 He was condemned to row in a ship that used sails and oars. A Roman galley was a single-decked ship, but the Romans also had triremes – with three banks of oars.

647 Anthony Babington conspired to assassinate Elizabeth and set her cousin, Mary, Queen of Scots, on the throne. The letters Babington sent to Mary in Fotheringhay Castle were intercepted by Walsingham's spies. Babington and Mary were both executed.

648 Queen Mary I preceded Elizabeth and King James I (VI of Scotland) followed her.

649 James Wolfe.

650 Simon de Montfort. Born in France of a French family, he came to settle in England in 1231.

651 Queen Isabella of Spain financed the expedition, so Columbus claimed the land he discovered for Spain.

652 Jan Smuts.

653 William Pitt, Earl of Chatham (1708–1778) and William Pitt the Younger (1759–1806). There was also George Grenville (1712–1770) and William Wyndham Grenville (1759–1834).

654 King George IV and King William IV.

655 He was the son of Mary and a cousin (not a first cousin) of Elizabeth.

656 The Prince Regent ruled during the later years of King George III's reign because the King, his father, was incapable. He later became George IV. The Prince Consort was Queen Victoria's husband, Albert of

Saxe-Coburg. A prince regent reigns in place of the reigning monarch, and a prince consort is the title of the husband of a reigning sovereign and does not himself rule.

657 The Duke of Wellington, who was made a duke in 1814.

658 Duke of Marlborough, who was made a duke in 1702.

659 Cardinal Wolsey gave Hampton Court to King Henry VIII. Wolsey had had the palace built, and it became Henry VIII's favourite residence.

660 The island is Iona. Columba settled there and founded a monastery. His monks acted as missionaries on the neighbouring islands and on the Scottish mainland.
St. Columba was born in Ireland and came from a line of Irish kings. He also founded several monasteries in Ireland.

661 The *Henry Grace à Dieu* ('Great Harry') in which Henry VIII sailed for France in 1520.

662 Nelson's flagship the *Victory*, at the Battle of Trafalgar 1805.

General knowledge 11

663 C. S. Forester.

664 John Buchan.

665 A special milking shed where cows are milked four or six at a time. The cows are milked by means of a machine.

666 A building which contains a hop-drying kiln.

667 A cobra. It cannot hear, and moves in rhythm to the movements of the snake charmer.

668 Any entertainment with a set dance routine, but mainly in ballet. A choreographer creates the dances for ballet, modern dance or musical shows. He seldom dances in his own shows. He invents the idea, and a dance company carries it out. He must know dancing, music and theatre techniques.

669 In the Tower of London.

670 In Westminster Abbey.

671 A railway that has only one rail. It can either run above the track or hang freely from wheels on a rail. Tokyo built a monorail for the Olympic Games and New York built one for the World Fair held there.

672 A person who collects or makes a study of sea-shells.

673 A musician, or someone concerned with music.

674 A sailor, or someone concerned with navigation.

675 The Ganges.

676 Tibet. It lies on a high plateau that averages about 16,000 feet above sea level. The highest mountain in the world, Mt. Everest (29,000 ft), lies to the south of the plateau.

677 The Koran is the sacred book of the Moslems. Moslems believe that the Archangel Gabriel revealed the message of God to Mohammed a little at a time between A.D. 610 and 632, and it is recorded in the Koran. It is about the same size as the New Testament. It contains verses grouped into 114 chapters called *suras*.

678 It is America's major space and rocket research centre, serving as the starting point for America's first space explorations.

679 He flew a home-made kite during a thunderstorm. A bolt of lightning struck the kite-wire and travelled down to a key fastened at the end, where it caused a spark.

680 It produces shock waves that cause sonic bangs.

681 John Henry Cardinal Newman wrote the poem, and Sir Edward Elgar composed the music.

682 Gustav Holst.

Famous characters

683 A footprint in the sand – it was that of Man Friday. *Robinson Crusoe* was written by Daniel Defoe.

684 He rubbed his old lamp. *Aladdin and the Wonderful*

Lamp is an old oriental tale.

685 She bathed in flames of a pillar of fire in an extinct volcano.

686 They come from Abel Magwitch (alias Provis), the escaped convict.

687 In the stories by Sir Arthur Conan Doyle, Sherlock Holmes lived in Baker Street (No. 221B).

688 Dr. Watson.

689 The palace was in Sicilia.

690 It was called Thornfield Hall.

691 *Alice in Wonderland* (by Lewis Carroll).

692 *Treasure Island* (by Robert Louis Stevenson).

693 Merlin is the magician, and Morgan le Fay is Arthur's fairy sister.

694 (i) The Ancient Mariner. (ii) The sailors hang the albatross round his neck.

695 Jo, Meg, Beth and Amy (March).

696 Athos, Porthos and Aramis are the 'Three Musketeers' and d'Artagnan is their companion.

697 Don Quixote, the title character in the book by Cervantes, tried to enact his fantasy world of knightly chivalry and had many absurd adventures.

698 Huckleberry Finn, the title character in a book by Mark Twain, was a youth without domestic ties who lived an open-air life on and around the Mississippi River in the United States. Mark Twain was the pen name of Samuel Langhorne Clemens.

699 H. G. Wells wrote *The History of Mr Polly*.

700 James Joyce, the author of the book. In it, Joyce describes his efforts to free himself from every tie in order to develop a conscience for his time through art. He called himself 'Stephen Daedalus'.

More about Knight Books

Ask your local bookseller or at your
public library, for details of other Knight Books,
or write to the Editor-in-Chief,
Knight Books, Arlen House, Salisbury Road,
Leicester LE1 7QS

Among the famous titles available in Knight Books are

Helen Dore Boylston
SUE BARTON – STUDENT NURSE

Elizabeth Goudge
LINNETS AND VALERIANS

Patricia Lynch
THE TURF-CUTTER'S DONKEY

Baroness Orczy
THE SCARLET PIMPERNEL

Felix Salten
BAMBI

Jean Webster
DADDY-LONG-LEGS

Charles Nordhoff and James Norman Hall
MUTINY ON THE BOUNTY